CHICKENS

A step-by-step guide to choosing and keeping hens

LAURA BRYANT

ARCTURUS

ARCTURUS

This edition published in 2011 by Arcturus Publishing Limited
26/27 Bickels Yard, 151–153 Bermondsey Street,
London SE1 3HA

ISBN: 978-1-84837-750-9
AD001677EN

Printed in Singapore

The Fell Types are digitally reproduced by Igino Marini. www.iginomarini.com

CONTENTS

INTRODUCTION

Eggs and chicken meat are staple foods all around the world. They are both versatile ingredients in a meal and extremely nutritious. Yet, while they are enormously popular, the quality of chicken eggs and meat purchased in supermarkets for home cooking and used in many restaurants has been subject to a lot of criticism.

In fact, it is the popularity of these foods that is responsible for the decline in quality in the first place. Chickens have been farmed intensively for many years in order for the supply to meet the demand, and also to keep the price as low as possible in the many supermarket price wars that are conducted. Intensive farming has an extremely detrimental effect not only on the life of the chickens that

are subjected to it but also on the flavour of the final product that the consumer purchases.

However, things are changing. People are beginning to realize that it is more ethical and puts much tastier food on the table if you purchase chicken and eggs that have been raised in a free-range, organic environment as opposed to being battery farmed and fed with growth stimulants and antibiotic drugs. It may be a little bit more expensive, but the quality of the produce is so much better that the quantity needed is usually less, so it is possible for the price to balance out.

Supermarkets have had to accept that many consumers care about where their food has come from, not only from a personal perspective but also due to a growing recognition that a chicken that is supplying us with food is entitled to a decent life as much as we are. This change in view has also meant that the number of people wishing to raise their own chickens for eggs and for meat is increasing dramatically. There is no better way to know exactly where your food is coming from than to tend it yourself in your back garden.

KEEPING CHICKENS

Keeping chickens is an age-old activity and one that anyone can do successfully if they follow the basic rules.

Chickens are very pleasant creatures to have in the garden and if you purchase the correct breed they can be pets as much as producers of food. They are gentle birds, and if cared for in the right way they will be happy to be handled by adults and children alike. The pleasure of eating eggs that have been freshly laid that morning, rather than purchasing them from a shop where they could be more than a month old, is something that once experienced you will want to repeat again and again. Eating a tasty roast chicken that you know has lived happily in your garden, doing exactly as it wished in a wide, open space, will satisfy not just your stomach but also your peace of mind.

This aim of this book is to give the prospective backyard chicken keeper a comprehensive view of what is involved in rearing your own flock of chickens, and how to get the best out of them – as members of the family, as egg producers and as a source of meat. Simple hints and tips on natural and artificial egg incubation and making a chick brooder, through to feeding, wing clipping and what to do with a broody hen, are all covered in easy-to-follow sections.

Raising chickens does take commitment and even though they are independent creatures, they do need care and attention on a daily basis. You have to be prepared to go out to feed and water them in all weathers and to know how to spot problems or diseases before they become out of control. You also need to ensure that you have someone you can rely on to care for your flock properly when you go on holiday as your chickens will not be able to fend for themselves.

Once this is part of your routine you will not look back, and in time people around you will be asking you more and more questions as they start to think about raising chickens themselves!

PART 1

GETTING STARTED

CHICKEN BREEDS

There are numerous chicken breeds, so you can choose your birds from a range of shapes, sizes and colours. Some breeds are more suited to the needs of a self-sufficient gardener or smallholder than others, such as those that farms servicing the big supermarkets use.

Over the thousands of years since chickens became domesticated, hundreds of breeds have been developed with just a few main criteria in mind – improved egg production, better-quality meat, dual-purpose breeds – producing both good-quality eggs and good-quality meat – and, finally, chickens that can adapt to different climates, not only those found within one country but around the world, as chicken is a global product. However,

selecting your type of chicken will not be too difficult because out of the many chicken breeds worldwide there are only a handful that specifically suit the needs and lifestyle of home chicken-keeping.

When choosing your bird(s), keep in mind that no breed is perfect. As is the case in most animal species, each chicken is an individual with its own temperament and personality. Even if you get a chicken from a breed that is meant to be friendly and docile, there is a chance that the one you take home has a bit of an attitude problem! Just remember to treat your new birds as members of your household, and with a bit of love and care they will end up feeling at home, bringing you a lot of pleasure both as pets and as a source of food.

CHICKEN CHAT

The first domesticated chicken probably originated over 8,000 years ago in what is today known as Thailand. It is believed to have been domesticated from a form of the wild species *Gallus gallus* (junglefowl), which is still prevalent today in much of Asia. It is also thought that there was more than one species domesticated in different locations around Asia, and that it is unlikely all domestic chickens stem from one breed.

GOOD FOR BEGINNERS

Orpington This is probably the best breed when you are starting out, especially if it is eggs you are interested in. Their abundance of feathers gives them an almost fluffy appearance, and they come in buff, black, blue and white. They are great for family gardens as they are calm, submissive birds that do not mind being handled. They will lay about 150 good-quality eggs in a year. Their downside is that if you introduce other breeds to your garden at a later date they will show a tendency to feather peck, especially if you acquire birds from the flightier breeds.

Rhode Island Red Originating from the US state of Rhode Island, these birds were first developed in the 1890s. They are classic garden hens as they are strong and can live in a multitude of environments.

As long as they are well cared for they will produce meat with a lovely flavour and an abundance of eggs. The main thing to watch out for with Rhode Islands is that they can grow to a fair size and need a coop and run to match that.

Other good breeds for beginners include:

Hybrids Most hybrids with either of the two above breeds in their parentage are a good starting point as hybrids tend to lay throughout the year, are usually easier to tame and generally make better pets for the family garden.

GOOD GARDEN LAYERS

Leghorn This chicken, which originates from Leghorn, Italy, is now a common egg layer worldwide. Although they were originally white they are now available in a range of colours, but all have white earlobes, yellow legs and red eyes. The modern-day hybrid battery hen was bred from Leghorns because of their excellent productivity and their ability to adapt to the harshest of weather and living conditions. They will lay in abundance, rarely go broody and will eat all the slugs your garden has to offer. However, on the downside, they can be rather noisy and are a bit timid – especially in busy households, such as those with children.

Sussex This breed is one of the oldest and really does look like the archetypal chicken. As the name suggests, it originates from the county of Sussex in the UK and it is as popular today as when it was first bred. Sussex chickens come in brown, buff, light red, speckled, silver and white. They can lay over 250 eggs a year and are just as happy in the confined space of a small garden plot as they are free-range. One of the main plus points about the Sussex is that they rarely go broody.

Pekin This is a true bantam (see pages 15–16) and, as its name suggests, it originates from China. It is a spectacular-looking hen with swan-white feathers. They make fantastic pets for children as they are easily tamed and due to their beauty, they also make marvellous show birds. Pekins come in a variety of colours – lavender, buff, black and speckled to name a few. As far as production goes, you can expect about 150 smallish eggs from your Pekin in a year.

Other good garden layers include:

Brahmas They make a fantastic show in the garden and are very easy-going; they can be handled without any difficulty.

GOOD DUAL-PURPOSE BREEDS
If you are looking at keeping chickens as a step towards self-sufficiency and like the thought of having a roast chicken from your back garden as well as eggs, then a dual-purpose breed is definitely worth considering. They may not produce quite as many eggs as their egg-specialist relatives, but they definitely combine the best of both worlds.

Australorp Developed in Australia using a high percentage of Black Orpington, the Australorp will lay around 200 eggs a year as well as giving you plenty

of meat on a healthy adult bird. Like the Orpington, they are great for a family garden as they do not mind being handled and are unperturbed by other breeds or family pets. Another upside to keeping them at home is that they are not very good flyers, so fencing does not need to be especially high. Although they are content in runs, Australorps are happiest, and at their most productive, if allowed to roam free-range.

Barred Plymouth Rock These originate from New England, USA, and have been bred since the 1850s. They are popular as a small flock breed and are friendly, able to stand cold winters and make excellent mothers, if you wish to start breeding. Their large eggs (of which they can lay around 200 in a year) and yellow skin (which is ideal for roasting) make them perfect contenders if you wish to get

the most from your breed. The downside to Plymouth Rocks is that you have to collect their eggs regularly otherwise they can be prone to broodiness.

Other good dual-purpose breeds:

New Hampshire A relatively new breed (1930s) originating from the USA, New Hampshire chickens are slightly better for meat than eggs.

Rhode Island Red See page 11.

TABLE-SPECIFIC BREEDS
Table-specific breeds, or broilers as they are also known, can be a little difficult to raise in a small garden or yard as these breeds are specifically created to grow rapidly and therefore struggle to make the most of the free-range facilities you are providing. However, you will definitely be giving them a better quality of life than they

usually get when reared for commercial meat purposes. Broiler breeds – Hubbards, Ixworth and Cornish Rock – will be the most economical if they are wanted solely for the purpose of meat as they will be ready sooner than a dual-purpose bird. The downside to this is that the meat from table-specific breeds is not usually as succulent and tasty as if you had reared a free-range dual-purpose breed such as the Australorp or the Barred Plymouth Rock.

THE RECOMMENDED CHOICE

For the purpose of keeping chickens at home a dual-purpose breed is definitely best. You will get fantastic eggs on a daily basis and some meat of great quality – maybe not enough to be totally self-sufficient, but it is a start.

CHICKEN SIZES

As you have already discovered, chickens come in various sizes and this is something to consider before you make a final choice as to which breed to get. Will the chickens you are thinking of acquiring grow too large in relation to the size of the area you will be keeping them in?

Bantams are a good choice for the garden keeper as they are naturally smaller in size. The name derives from the Indonesian port called Bantam. When European sailors used to stock up on live fowl for homeward sea journeys they found the small native breeds of chicken found in South East Asia to be useful. Subsequently, any small type of chicken came to be known as a bantam.

Nowadays, you can get bantam versions of most chicken breeds – sometimes referred to as miniature – and they are usually about 25 per cent the size of the standard breed. They are ideal as pets or for being raised in smallholdings, gardens and yards. Caring for bantams is just the same as caring for a standard size chicken and they eat the same feed. The drawback, obviously, is that even though bantams are egg layers, because of their smaller stature their eggs are also smaller than a standard hen's egg – usually half to one-third the size.

PART 2

STARTING WITH A FERTILIZED EGG

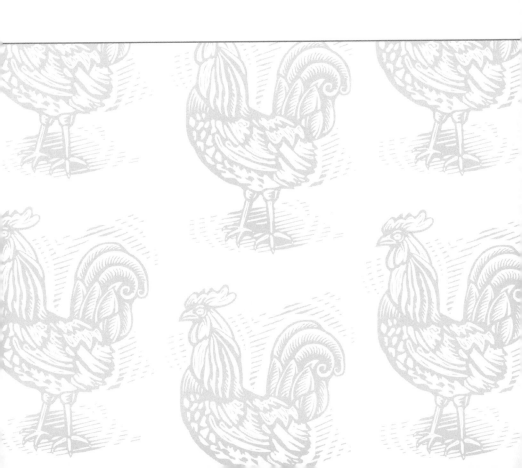

THE FERTILIZED EGG

Eggs start their life as just a yolk in the hen's ovary. When the egg is released from the ovary it passes into a funnel-shaped organ called the infundibulum – if the hen has mated with a cockerel this is where the sperm will be. If sperm is present the egg will be fertilized; either way it will continue down the funnel where it is covered with a membrane, structural fibres and egg white.

The shell membrane is the next thing to cover the egg, which forms and hardens in the shell gland ready to be laid. The shell is made from calcite, a crystalline form of calcium carbonate. The entire process from yolk to fully formed 'egg' takes about 24 hours. However, chickens do not like to lay their eggs at night and will hold on to them until the morning if necessary. Once the hen does lay she is ready to start the process all over again and, if she has been mated, may even have enough sperm stored inside her to fertilize another egg.

THE FERTILIZED EGG

If you wish to keep chickens and like the idea of starting with an egg and raising it into adulthood, then you need to acquire some fertilized eggs in the breed or breeds of your choice. Hens produce eggs with or without a cockerel around, but it is only the ones that have been fertilized by a male that have the possibility of becoming chicks that will grow to become part of your self-sufficient lifestyle.

Once you try it, you will discover that raising chickens from fertilized eggs is fun and interesting for adults and children alike. It's a great way to involve younger family members in your chicken-keeping and can help to teach them about conception and the life-cycle of living things.

ACQUIRING YOUR EGGS

Spring is probably the best time to think about hatching your own eggs as it is the natural mating season, so purchasing fertilized eggs from your local poultry farmer or hatchery will not be a problem as they will be in plentiful supply. Hatching eggs vary in price depending on what breeds the suppliers have available, but they average at around £3 per egg for a common breed.

If you are starting off without any other chickens you need the eggs to have been 'set'. This means that the eggs have been sat on by the hen that laid them to start the incubating process

going. The eggs then need to be placed in an incubator no later than three days after purchasing them.

Pages 22–32 explain in more detail the artificial hatching process, including step-by-step instructions on making your own incubator for your eggs to develop and hatch in.

The following are good tips to remember when you are selecting your eggs from the poultry farm or hatchery in order to get the healthiest chicks possible:

- The best egg size to choose is somewhere in the middle. If they are too big they have a tendency to hatch poorly, while eggs that are too small will result in small chicks which may not be hardy enough to make it into adulthood, or will not provide the quality and quantity of produce that you are hoping for.

CHICKEN CHAT

Hens will wait until there are a few fertilized eggs before they sit on them. Eggs can last up to two weeks without being incubated while the hen lays more eggs. Once the setting process begins all eggs will develop at the same rate, as though they had all been laid at the same time.

- Do not choose eggs with cracks and thin shells as damaged eggs stand a high chance of not hatching.

- Avoid eggs with dirty or marked shells. Not only might they contaminate the chicks on hatching, but they must not be cleaned either, because eggshells have a protective coating on them called the 'bloom' which stops the chicks inside being infected with diseases.

NATURAL SETTING AND HATCHING

If you already have chickens, setting and hatching a few eggs naturally seems like the obvious choice. However, it is not just a case of placing your newly purchased eggs in the coop and leaving your chickens to it; you need to have a broody hen in your flock at the same time that you want your eggs set. Natural hatching does require a little more attention to your birds, and often more space, too: if you want to set eggs with more than one broody hen, for example, you either have to place all the eggs under the hens at the same time, or else keep them out of sight and sound of one another so that the hen whose eggs have yet to hatch is not disturbed by the tweeting of the newly hatched chicks. See pages 120–122 for more information on breeding from your hens.

USING AN INCUBATOR

HEN HINTS – CANDLING

Whether you are incubating your eggs naturally or artificially, it is worth using a process called 'candling' in order to see if the eggs you have are fertilized, as not every egg will have been. Candling means holding the egg up to a light bright enough to penetrate the shell in order to see what is going on inside. If the egg has been fertilized you will see a dark red spot with veins radiating out in every direction. See page 32 for more information.

Once in possession of your set eggs, if you don't have any hens to hatch them, you will need to put them in an artificial incubator.

The important part of the incubation process is keeping the outside temperature and the humidity of the incubator constant. Incubators are a wise investment and have been used in some form for over 2,000 years.

The main factors that you need to get exactly right in the incubating process are temperature, humidity, position and movement. If any of these are not exactly right the likelihood of you hatching healthy chicks, or indeed any at all, is slim.

YOUR INCUBATOR

If you are handy with simple tools you can build your own incubator, following the step-by-step instructions on pages 26–29. If not, you will need to purchase one.

The size and type of the

incubator you purchase depends on how many eggs you wish to incubate in one go and also whether or not you will be incubating more eggs in the future. Ones that have separate incubating and hatching sections are ideal if you are going to be continuously setting and hatching eggs at different stages. Single unit incubators are better if all your eggs start at the same stage.

The two main types of incubators are 'forced-air' and 'still-air'. For home rearing a small number of chicks still-air, single units are probably going to be adequate for your needs. However, forced-air can give better results as they automatically keep temperature and humidity more constant. Talk to your retailer before purchasing and do not choose your incubator on price alone, either because it seems like a bargain or because it is an

> ## HATCHING HINTS
>
> Approximately three days prior to hatching, insert a layer of cheesecloth on the screen, placing it beneath the eggs. This will make the incubator much easier to clean after the hatching process is complete.

expensive all-singing all-dancing design. Evaluate your needs and buy your incubator on that basis alone.

The following are points that should be followed in order to get the most from your hatch:

- Place the incubator in a room that is not often used, which will make it easier to keep the temperature constant.

- The ideal room temperature is 24°C (75°F) with a relative humidity of 60 per cent.

- It is possible to buy a hygrometer fairly cheaply to keep an eye on the humidity inside the incubator.

- The incubator needs to be sanitized and left on for at least 24 hours prior to putting the eggs in so that the temperature and humidity levels are correct.

- The temperature in the incubator must be 37.5°C (99.5°F) in a forced-air and 38.5°C (101°F) in a still-air incubator – any deviation above or below this will result in a poor hatch.

- To get an accurate thermometer reading, place the bulb of the thermometer at the same height as the top of the egg if it is lying in horizontal position, or 7–14 cm (3–5½ in) from the top if vertical. Do not let the thermometer touch either the incubator or the egg as the reading will be inaccurate.

- Eggs must be turned at least 4–6 times a day during incubation, but do not turn them during the last three days before hatching as the embryos are moving into hatching position. If the eggs need to be turned by hand it may be helpful to mark each one with an A on one side and a B on the other so it is easier to determine if all eggs have been turned. Make sure these marks are made in pencil – and when turning ensure that your hands have been washed and are free of any greasy or dusty residue.

- Take extra care when turning the eggs in the first week as the developing embryos will have delicate blood vessels that will rupture if they are jarred or shaken severely.

• The air vents should be kept almost fully open during the latter stages of incubation in order to keep the eggs from overheating and to ensure that they have an adequate oxygen supply as they incubate and start to hatch. This is another reason why the room temperature is so important. If the power supply to the incubator is lost for some reason and the incubator is in a hot and stuffy room, the eggs are going to be more vulnerable to suffocation than would be the case if the incubator were in a room with a constant temperature of 24°C (75°F).

CLEANING YOUR INCUBATOR

Whether your incubator is homemade or shop-bought, neglecting to keep it in tip-top condition can result in a significant reduction in eggs that hatch into live, healthy chicks. Microbial infections arising from a build-up of bacteria caused by not sanitizing your incubator need to be avoided.

The cleaning process should be part of standard operating procedures and it is imperative that incubators are disinfected after each and every hatch.

Begin by removing all eggshells, feathers, dust and so forth with a dustpan and brush or a vacuum cleaner. Once all the debris has been removed, wash the incubator using a mild solution of non-biological washing powder and warm water. Use a cloth and also an old toothbrush in order to get into any hard-to-reach areas. Follow by rinsing with a mild disinfectant solution and let the incubator dry naturally. When it is completely dry you can turn the unit on, re-regulate the temperature and begin the incubation to hatching process all over again.

BUILDING YOUR OWN INCUBATOR

Building your own incubator can be a lot easier than you might think. If you are able to obtain a polystyrene cooler box this will make the whole process a lot simpler as the main set-up of the incubator is done for you.

Another advantage to using a polystyrene box is that it is the perfect material for regulating temperature. It will insulate your eggs, but at the same time it is easy to add additional ventilation.

YOU WILL NEED

light socket with cord
large polystyrene cooler with lid
marker pen
pen knife
dimmer switch (for a table
    lamp, not a wall light)
20 × 28 cm (8 × 11 in) piece
    of glass
tape or wood glue
small screwdriver
small plastic fan
small bowl of water
thermometer (in clear plastic
    sleeve)
25- or 15-watt light bulb

INSTRUCTIONS

1. Place the light socket upside down on top of the polystyrene cooler lid. Draw a circle around it and, using a pen knife, cut out a hole.

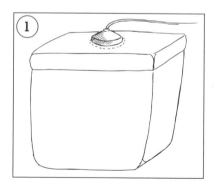

2. Place the light socket inside the hole, making it larger with your knife if necessary. Allow the cord to stick out of the top and make sure you can reach the on/off switch from the outside of the box. Add the dimmer switch to the cord to allow you to control the temperature inside your incubator. Place a 25-watt light bulb into the socket, or a 15-watt if your incubator is quite small.

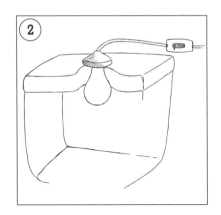

3. Cut out a square in the side of the cooler, slightly smaller than your piece of glass. Using either tape or wood glue, attach the glass to the outside of the box over the square you have just cut. By fixing it to the outside, not the inside, you will create a more securely sealed window which is also safer as there is no risk of the chicks injuring themselves against the sharp edges of the glass.

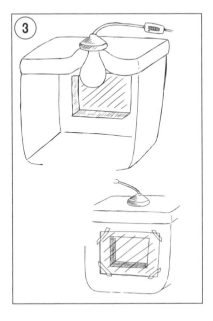

4. Punch a few holes in the side of the cooler, using a small screwdriver. These holes will provide your eggs with some ventilation. Fill a small bowl with water and place it inside the incubator, as this will help to control the humidity. Place a thermometer that is enclosed in a clear plastic sleeve inside the incubator, making sure that it is in a location that is clearly visible from the window. The base of the thermometer needs to be at the same level as the eggs when you place them inside. Check again that the on/off switch and dimmer switch on your light fitting are both fully functioning.

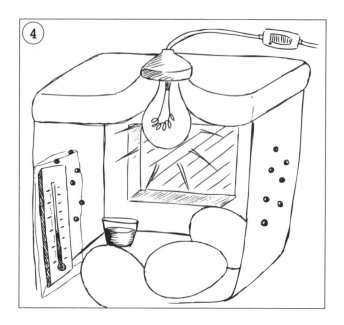

5. Place a small plastic fan in the back corner of the incubator. This makes the air circulate inside the box, thus helping to regulate the temperature. You will need to make a hole in the corner in order to allow the flex from the fan to pass through, insulating the hole with tape when you are finished. Close the lid. Now turn on the light and the fan and allow them to run for several hours, keeping a close eye on the temperature. You might need to tape over the ventilation holes if the temperature drops too low; if it gets too hot, you can add further ventilation holes. You can also control the temperature by adjusting the brightness of the lamp, using the dimmer switch. Remember that the temperature must be 37.5°C (99.5°F) in an incubator where you are using a fan.

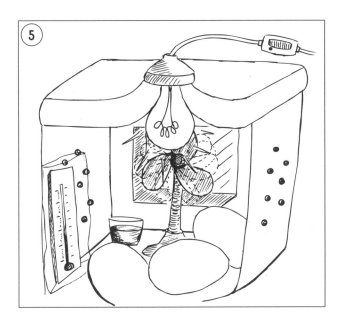

THE STAGES OF HATCHING

Within the first 24 hours of the 21-day cycle, the eggshell hardens. By the second day, the chicken brain, eye, tail, wing and leg somites start to develop.

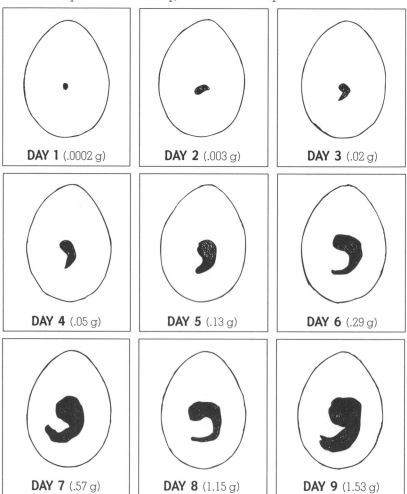

DAY 1 (.0002 g)　　**DAY 2** (.003 g)　　**DAY 3** (.02 g)

DAY 4 (.05 g)　　**DAY 5** (.13 g)　　**DAY 6** (.29 g)

DAY 7 (.57 g)　　**DAY 8** (1.15 g)　　**DAY 9** (1.53 g)

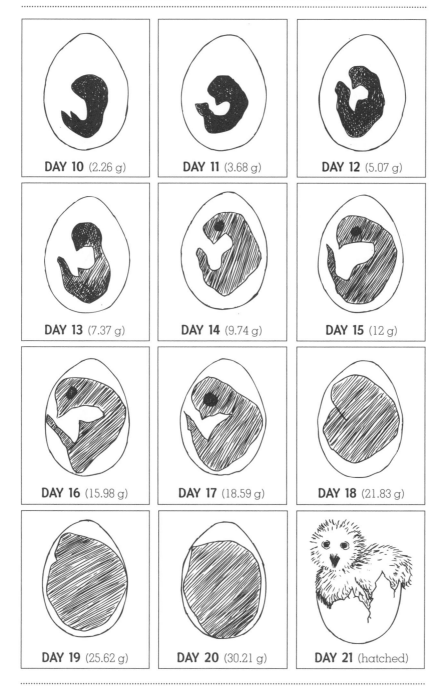

DAY 10 (2.26 g) **DAY 11** (3.68 g) **DAY 12** (5.07 g)

DAY 13 (7.37 g) **DAY 14** (9.74 g) **DAY 15** (12 g)

DAY 16 (15.98 g) **DAY 17** (18.59 g) **DAY 18** (21.83 g)

DAY 19 (25.62 g) **DAY 20** (30.21 g) **DAY 21** (hatched)

CANDLING – WHAT TO LOOK FOR

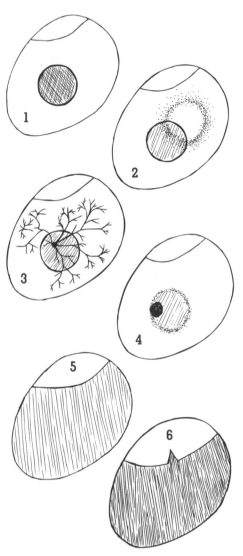

1. If the egg is clear when candled with no areas of red, then either the egg is infertile or the embryo suffered an early death.

2. If the egg is clear with a pale red blood ring, then it was fertile but the embryo was subject to an early death.

3. If you can see many little blood vessels within the shell the egg is fertile.

4. If a red or black blob or staining can be seen, this is another sign of early death.

5. A dark outline that is not well-defined could possibly mean late death at 11–16 days. However, it is worth giving an egg like this a little more time.

6. If you see a dark outline with defined detail and a bill in the air pocket, this is a live embryo that will hatch in the next 24–48 hours.

PART 3

YOUR NEW CHICK

THE HATCHING PROCESS

Remember that, as in nature, there is a chance that some eggs will not hatch, or if they do the chick inside will not be strong enough to survive into adulthood. If 60–70 per cent of your eggs hatch healthy chicks, you are doing extremely well.

After taking good care of your eggs, watching them hatch is a truly magical experience and one that the whole family can share in, as it is a great lesson in life-cycles and nurturing.

The hatching should start at around day 21, when you will start to hear the sound of the chicks pecking away at the shell of the egg that has been their home, their food and their life source for the past few weeks. At this point, bring the temperature of the incubator down to 35°C (95°F).

As the eggs start hatching, increase the humidity to 65 per cent and leave them alone. The best way to regulate humidity is to place a small bowl of water in one corner of the incubator. Do not touch the eggs or attempt to help any of the hatchlings out of their shells.

This is a natural process and if they are strong and healthy, they will free themselves in the end.

It is at the point when your first egg begins to hatch that you should get your brooder (see page 38) set up and cleaned, ready to move the new hatchlings into once the hatching process is complete. You will also need to provide chick feed and a waterer.

Remove any shell debris as each chick enters the world and spend some time just watching this magical event take place. Leave the chicks in the incubator for a little while so that their feathers can dry out – they may be sticky as a result of conditions that are too humid or too dry. Once all your chicks are fluffy and dry they are ready to be moved into the brooding box.

NEWBORN CHICK

If your chicks had been incubated by a hen and had

CHICK CHAT

The greatest number of yolks ever found in a single chicken egg was nine.

therefore hatched naturally, their mother hen would take on all the care duties herself and in a short amount of time the new chicks would be mimicking her actions and feeding without any problem.

When there is no hen around and the chicks have been incubated artificially, the subsequent care of these new and vulnerable creatures is all down to you. The most important thing after ensuring that they are kept warm in their brooder is getting them used to water. Do this by dipping their beaks in their water dish. This will also help them to understand where in the brooder their water dish is located.

SEXING YOUR CHICKS

Once your hatchlings are out of their protective shells, they are even more in need of your help in rearing them into strong adults.

The next step may be to sex your new chicks in order to find out if they are hens or cocks. Note that this is quite a task and something that you may need help and advice with from a trained expert. However, if you are up for the challenge, this is how you go about it.

SEX-LINKED BREEDS

If you have hybrid breeds as opposed to pure breeds, the task of chick sexing is much easier as your chicks probably have specially bred feathers that help you to distinguish whether they are male or female. These are known as 'sex-linked' chickens and your hatchery or local poultry farm can advise you what to look for when you purchase your eggs. The females of sex-linked breeds usually have longer wing pinfeathers.

VENT SEXING

In the absence of sex-linked distinguishing features, the only other way of discovering the sex of your chicks is by using a technique called 'vent sexing'. This involves squeezing the faeces out of the chick, which thereby opens up its anal vent, allowing someone with a trained eye to see if the chick has a small 'bump'. If it does, this means that it is male.

BE PATIENT!

The above method may not appeal to you, and if you do not have or want sex-linked eggs and are unable to find someone to vent sex your chicks you are probably best advised to wait until they are around six weeks old, when secondary characteristics specific to either male or female start to appear. Usually the combs and wattles of males become larger in size than those of a female hen, and the male's head will start to look more masculine. The hen's head, on the other hand, will stay small and rather more refined in appearance.

In some breeds the feathers of each sex will develop a colour specific to them and this is something to ask your hatchery or poultry farm about when you purchase your eggs.

HEN HINTS

Do note that in urban environments having a cockerel crowing as soon as dawn breaks is not ideal for you or your neighbours. Therefore, you may need to dispatch all the male chicks, which you may find no easy feat in practical terms and also an emotionally tough thing to do. There may be breeders willing to take some males from you, but if not, they must be dispatched in the most humane way possible. This is a major consideration when deciding whether to rear chickens from chicks or eggs. See pages 124–128 for more information.

CARING FOR YOUR CHICKS

Newborn chicks need a lot of care in order to grow into the strong egg-laying hens that you require for your garden. The first thing to acquire, or make (see pages 40–41) is a brooder. This is a heated box that keeps the space inside it at a constant temperature by means of a heat lamp.

Even though the chicks look small, it is important that each chick has 22 x 22 cm (8 x 8 in) – or the equivalent area – of floor space in the brooder, from day one until six weeks of age.

If the brooder you obtain has been used previously, make sure you clean it thoroughly before adding the chicks to it. Their immune systems are not yet sufficiently strong to fight diseases, so it is always better to be on the safe side and ensure their new home is as sanitized as it can be.

For the first week of the chicks' lives, the temperature should be kept at above 32°C (89.5°F); in the second week the temperature should be brought down to 26–29°C (79–84°F) and in week three reduced a further 5 degrees to 21–24°C (70–75°F).

It is imperative that your new chicks have a constant supply of fresh water to drink. The water should be changed and the waterer cleaned on a daily basis. An important point to remember when it comes to deciding what type of vessel to store the water in is that it should not be of a size that could be turned into a bathing pool by the chick. If the chick gets wet this could be disastrous as being so young they will find it hard to get themselves dry and warm again. The best thing to do is either invest in an automatic waterer or use a very shallow dish and raise it off the ground so that they are unable to immerse themselves in it.

As far as food is concerned, for the first 6–8 weeks chicks should be fed on a starter mash which can be purchased from your local feed dealer. However, if you are unable to obtain this in the first few days, instant oatmeal, flaked infant cereal or other whole-grain cereals will suffice. You can put whole grains such as wheat, barley or oats into a blender and grind them lightly – do not blend completely to a powder as the feed should have a gritty texture to it. Whereas fully-grown chickens can be left with a constant supply of food and will stop eating when they have had enough, chicks should be given small amounts of feed regularly throughout the day. See page 42 for more information.

CHICK TROUBLESHOOTING

• Are your chicks active, with a good appetite? If the answer is yes, their needs are being fulfilled and they should keep growing into strong adolescent hens.

• Are your chicks panting, standing away from each other with their beaks open and lacking movement? They may be too hot. Try making some air holes in the brooder or reducing the wattage of the lamp.

• Are your chicks huddled together in the corner of the brooder? They may be too cold, so look at upping the wattage of the lamp bulb, closing any air holes or shutting off any draughts in the brooder that may be causing discomfort to your juvenile birds.

MAKING YOUR OWN CHICK BROODER

A chick brooder is essential as a place where you can put your newly hatched chicks to keep them warm and safe. You can buy a variety of ready-made brooders, or you could have a go at making this simple one yourself.

YOU WILL NEED

1 large cardboard box
duct tape
newspaper
a piece of wood
light with 40-watt bulb
waterer
chick feeder

1. Find yourself a cardboard box that is large enough to comfortably accommodate your chicks.

2. Strengthen the bottom of the box by placing duct tape across the middle and around the edges. This will help to give the box support if it gets wet, or if you wish to move it to a new position.

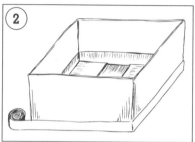

3. Next, line the bottom of the box with some layers of newspaper so that it does not become soiled with droppings. You will need to change this paper each day as new chicks can be extremely messy.

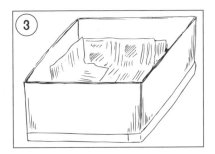

4. You will need to give your chicks some warmth, so hang a 40-watt bulb from the top of the brooder. The bulb must be at least 7.5 cm (3 in) from the bottom of the box and not too close to the sides to avoid the box catching fire. The best way is to place a piece of wood across the top of the box in the centre and wrap the cord of the light round it several times.

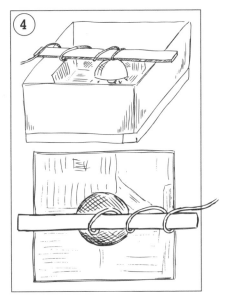

5. Now place a feeder and a waterer in the box, ideally at opposite ends so that the chicks do not scatter their food into the water.

BROODER MANAGEMENT

FLOORING
It is a good idea to use only newspaper on the floor of the brooder for the first couple of weeks. After this time you can change to a loose, absorbent mixture of wood shavings and straw, as it is better for their feet and posture than the smooth surface of newspaper.

FEEDING
Chicks need to be fed little and often in the first six weeks of their lives. Five times a day is sufficient to begin with, bringing it down to four times at six weeks and three times a day when they reach eight weeks of age.

Even though ready-made feeds are the best choice for providing the correct amount of nutrients for your chicks, try to stay away from feeds that are made with commercially

kept birds in mind, as these will contain a lot of extra additives. Use a basic grower feed supplemented at home with items such as chopped hard-boiled eggs, fish meal, milk and earthworms, making it as natural a feed as possible.

TEACHING CHICKS TO FEED
To begin with, scatter some feed over the floor to help the chicks learn how to eat. Change this to a hanging feeder as soon as possible in order to keep the feed cleaner.

KEEPING THEM CLEAN
Keep an eye on your newly hatched chicks for signs of dried excrement around the anus, this is called 'pasting up' and can be fatal to a chick. It can be caused by stress or a chill. Remove any excrement with a warm, wet cloth.

PART 4

YOUR ADOLESCENT HEN

HEN ANATOMY

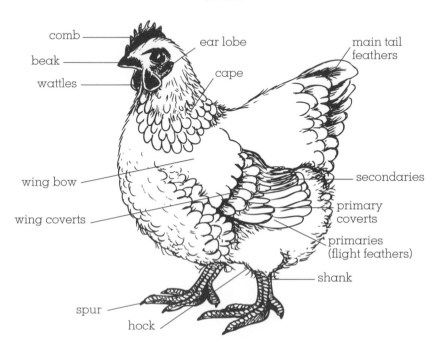

comb

beak

wattles

ear lobe

cape

main tail feathers

wing bow

wing coverts

secondaries

primary coverts

primaries (flight feathers)

shank

spur

hock

THE SIGN OF A HEALTHY HEN

When fully grown, a chicken should have a nice firm comb that does not flop to one side. It will be bright red when the chicken is laying. The eyes should be beady and bright, and the bird should be lean, active and alert. The scales on the legs and feet should be smooth, not raised. The colour of the legs is also a good indication of whether the chicken is laying. If they are yellow she is probably not laying, but if they are pale, almost white, the likelihood is that she has laid some eggs.

ADOLESCENT REARING INTO ADULTHOOD

Once your chicks are fully feathered and able to be independent they can be transferred to their outdoor home, either as the first chickens of your flock or as its newest additions. If female, they are known as pullets until they are a year old.

As the chicks are still young they will need to be kept warm and dry but there is no longer a need for a heat lamp; just keep them away from any draughts. A coop for rearing adolescents needs to be large enough for all the chicks to shelter in it if the weather is bad, and it will also need to accommodate the feeder and drinker. If an adult coop is to be used it is important to block off the nest boxes with cardboard. If the youngsters start out roosting in nest boxes

it is a habit that is almost impossible to break in later life, which will lead to dirty and partly incubated eggs – which completely defeats the object of keeping chickens in the first place.

INTRODUCTIONS TO EXISTING HENS

If you already have mature hens that are laying eggs, you will need to introduce your youngsters to them. However, this should not be done until they are at least 4–5 months old.

To begin with, keep them in separate pens but close together so that they become accustomed to the sight and smell of each other. It is also imperative that the existing hens are deloused and that the coop

HEN HINT

In order to get the maximum egg production when they reach adulthood, it is best to delay the sexual maturity of your pullets. This can be measured by the time of year, as an increase in day length encourages early sexual maturity of the adolescent. If the chicks are hatched between April and August they can be exposed to natural day length, as it starts to shorten halfway through the pullet's growth period. If you are raising just a few chickens at home, also consider hatching your eggs after March as less heat will be required to brood them.

VACCINATION

People who keep hens that have been incubated from eggs in their gardens rarely seem to vaccinate their new additions. This is a shame, as there are many diseases to which they are susceptible which can be prevented.

Chickens can usually be vaccinated at a reasonable price at your local veterinary surgery. However, if you decide against vaccinating because of this additional cost, make sure that the bare minimum you do is get your chickens wormed. Worming tablets and powder can be purchased cheaply online or through your local hatchery.

WHERE IS HOME?

Keep your pullets close to the coop for the first few days so that they understand where 'home' is – they can enjoy a free-range life a little later. Be patient, as the most important thing is getting them used to

that they eventually live in together has been cleaned very thoroughly so that the youngsters do not pick up any nasty parasites or diseases.

where to roost at night – and that's inside the coop, away from predators. If left to roam free at night, they would very quickly become dinner for a prowling fox.

If you are adding your youngsters to an already existing flock they should not have any problems learning where home is as they will simply mimic their elders. However, if your pullets are your first outdoor hens, you may have to give them some guidance about where they should roost. The best way to do this is to keep them locked in their coop the first day that you take them outside. Allow them to go outside for a couple of hours before dusk and then, as the light starts to fall, give them a helping hand in the direction of the coop and lock them in. You will only need to follow this procedure for one or two days before your pullets go into the coop of their own volition. Chickens

> **CHICKEN CHAT**
>
> Most eggs purchased from supermarkets or convenience stores, whether they are from barn-raised or free-range chickens, are generally more than 30 days old before they end up on your table. Try eating an egg that is less than 24 hours old and you will soon know why you have started keeping chickens!

are creatures of habit, so once this routine has been adopted they will continue to follow it.

You will also notice that they become agitated near sundown – they will do everything they can to get indoors before dark.

THE NEW HOME
Paying attention to detail when rearing adolescents is key to having strong, healthy hens that lay tasty eggs and give good meat. Although you

should keep their environment as clean as possible, they will also need to build up their own immune system. This will happen naturally once they join the flock, though introduction to the outside world and other flock members should be done gradually.

In the adolescents' new home it is also a good idea to have perches available so that they can roost above ground. This is a natural way for a bird to sleep and prevents them from roosting in their own muck which could lead to problems of ill health. Make sure that the perches are positioned to give each bird its own space and that they are at least 5 cm (2 in) thick so that they do not suffer from bent breastbones.

FEEDING

Keep your pullets on the chick feed as recommended by your local supplier until they are about four months old. At this point they can be moved on to a layer formula, which contains a higher level of calcium to help your hens produce eggs with strong shells. This is mostly for the hen's sake, as weak shells can break in the hen before she has had a chance to lay.

If you want to be as self-sufficient as possible you can also put your hens on home-made chicken feed from this age. There are both pros and cons to making your own feed. Some chicken keepers argue that home-made feed is not only cheaper than purchasing ready-made feed but also healthier, as you know exactly what is going into it. However, others take the view that only commercially-made feed, purchased from professional outlets, can give a flock the balanced daily nutritional requirements the chickens need to live healthy lives, lay good-quality eggs and produce tasty high-class meat.

NUTRITION

There are many resources both online and in poultry handbooks that give instructions on mixing your own feed. The procedure can be complex, so before you go ahead make sure you appreciate the time that needs to be allocated and that you understand your chickens' nutritional requirements.

There are certain minerals, vitamins and other substances that are crucial to the well-being of chickens:

Calcium This is vital in egg production as it helps the hen to produce strong and durable shells. Hens lacking in calcium will lay eggs that have thin shells, or maybe even lack shells altogether.

Grit As chickens have no teeth with which to grind down food, grit is an important aid to digestion. Without it your birds will find it difficult to break up their food. Once the grit is eaten it becomes lodged in the gizzard – the muscular, thick-walled part of the bird's stomach. Any food consumed will then pass through the grit, where it is ground up on its way through the digestive system.

Vitamin D This is needed to process calcium and phosphorus and also helps in the formation of a strong skeleton. Sunlight is a good source of vitamin D, but if your hens are not getting enough sun a supplement in your home-made feed may be necessary.

Riboflavin A deficiency in riboflavin can cause embryo death during the early stages of incubation, so it is important that it is present in your hens' diet if you wish to rear further chickens from their eggs. This vitamin is found in dairy products, leafy greens, yeast and liver. Many commercial feeds lack this vitamin.

Vitamin E This is needed for healthy birds that have good defences against diseases. It can be found in leafy greens and whole grains.

If you feel that making your own feed is too time-consuming and you will worry about getting it wrong, a good balance would be to purchase the main feed and then supplement this with healthy chicken snacks such as leafy vegetables and whole grains that can be dotted around the garden for them to peck at.

You will find more information on feeding chickens on pages 66–70.

CANNIBALISM

The idea of cannibalism among your flock is unsettling, but it is something that you may encounter when keeping and rearing chickens, especially in adolescent and laying flocks, and it can be difficult to control once it has started. The causes of cannibalism include overcrowding, nutrient deficiencies, inadequate ventilation, lack of water and the sight and smell of blood on an injured member of the flock.

Be sure to keep a close eye on your new garden flock and, if necessary, think about getting your chicks' beaks trimmed at your local hatchery prior to placing them in their new outdoor home. Beak trimming can be done at any time but could stress an adolescent hen if carried out when she is coming into production.

Luckily, most smallholders and backyard chicken keepers wish their hens to lead a life that is as free-range as possible. This in itself will keep a lot of the vitamin deficiencies and potential cannibalism issues at bay.

MAKING A HOME FOR YOUR BIRDS

If you have the space it is best to let your birds roam as freely as possible, within bounds of what is safe for the birds and suitable for you. Chickens that spend the majority of their time outdoors need less space indoors for roosting and nesting as they are only going to be inside to eat and sleep. If you are keeping your hens outside but 'in range', such as on a specific area of your lawn, it is worth considering a coop that is easily transportable so that you can give the land where it has been a chance to recover.

If your garden is also used for things besides chickens, such as growing vegetables, a children's play area or barbecues, you may want to enclose the outdoor area for your chickens to roam using a fencing system. These are all things to consider prior to purchasing or building a home for your chickens and also before you decide how many chickens you would like to keep, as space is a primary factor in a bird's well-being.

There are no hard and fast rules about how much space you need per chicken inside and out – people's opinions differ vastly, so it is worth doing some research by talking to other back-garden chicken keepers to see what has worked for them before making an informed decision. If you do not know anybody else personally there are plenty of forums online where you can put this up as a discussion topic. To start with, you could consider having about 65 x 65 cm (2 x 2 ft) – or the equivalent area – of space per chicken in a coop, based on each chicken having 70 x 70 cm (2.5 x 2.5 ft) of space outside.

LOCAL REGULATIONS

Another thing to bear in mind prior to embarking on chicken keeping is whether there are any restrictions in your area. First, check your deeds for any restrictions on the keeping of poultry and livestock. Secondly, you may need to check with your local authority if you plan to keep a cockerel as they can be deemed a noise pollutant, although that may depend more on how friendly you are, or want to stay, with your neighbours! If you are just thinking of keeping a handful of hens there should not be any restrictions. However, if there is a large number of birds you will have to contact the central government agency responsible for the environment and rural affairs and have them added to the poultry register.

BUILDING YOUR OWN COOP

If you wish to build your own coop it can be as simple or as detailed as you want. It is easiest to make the walls from timber as it is readily available and easy to nail together. If you make a sketch of your design, your local timber merchant will be able to work out how much you will need, recommend the most suitable type and cut the wood to size for you. Do double check your measurements thoroughly before going ahead and make sure that you have got your decimal points in the right places.

Flooring

Wood or dirt flooring are the best options. A dirt floor is easy – all you need to do is build directly on to the patch of land that is going to be the plot for your coop. If you are building onto grass, it will become dirt in no time. The downside, however, is that it is harder to shovel dirt and manure from it, and it will eventually turn to mud if you have not got your drainage right.

If you decide on wood flooring for your coop, you do not need to spend a lot of money on it as any old timber planks found at the local dump or offcuts that you can persuade your timber merchant to part with, will do. Underneath these planks you will need supporting joists which will need to rest on blocks or stones in each of the four corners. These should be sunk into the earth to make them as stable as possible. Wood floors are easier to clean and keep your birds off the ground, but they will rot eventually.

Windows

Even if your hens are going to be spending most of their daylight hours outside, it is still important for your hen coop to have windows for light and ventilation. They will also help you to keep an eye on what is going on inside without disturbing a roosting flock.

The pop-hole

For the entrance used by the chickens, known as the pop-hole, construct a door that can be opened and closed from the outside so that you can control their access to and from the coop. If your coop has a raised floor, place a ramp in front of the pop-hole so your chickens do not have to jump or fly up to the entrance. The best solution is to use a hinged door over the pop-hole which can then drop down to become the ramp.

Litter board

As most of the excrement will be below the perches, to make your life easier you can lay either a piece of polythene or a wooden board on the floor, both of which can be removed easily for cleaning.

HANDY HINTS FOR COOP BUILDING

Note that these are general guidelines only and specific measurements depend on the size of your plot, how many chickens you wish to keep and how much additional outside space they will have.

PLANNING

- Assess the area. Make sure the coop and the land it is going to stand on will not accumulate rain puddles. Higher ground is better if possible.

- Sketch out your design on paper. Include a door large enough for you to enter the coop and if possible make the coop high enough to stand up in. Place windows so that they are south-facing to aid with ventilation and natural sunlight.

- Map out the inside of the coop, allowing a correct ratio of nest boxes for your flock and enough perching space per bird. One nest box to every three or four birds should be adequate as well as 22–25 cm (8½–10 in) of perch length per chicken.

- Purchase all the building material you need, including boundary wire for the run as well as feeders, waterers and straw.

- The floor plan opposite will give you an idea of what you should be trying to achieve. If possible, build your nest box as part of the coop, but as an additional area that you can get to without having to enter the main coop. See pages 62–63 for more information.

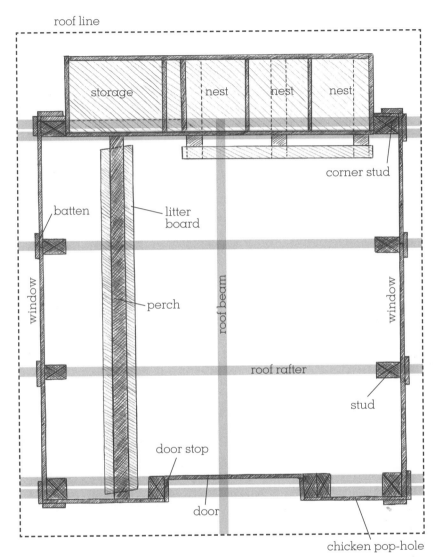

roof line

storage

nest

nest

nest

corner stud

batten

litter
board

window

perch

roof beam

window

roof rafter

stud

door stop

door

chicken pop-hole

Plan of a coop seen from above

BUILDING

• Try to construct your coop in an area where the front of the coop (where the door and windows are) can face to the south as this will give your birds the maximum hours of sunlight.

• Construct a sloping roof on your coop has so that rain does not run directly off the door.

• If you have open windows, make sure that they are securely covered with wire mesh to keep predators out. If you want your windows to be covered in order to help with heat and ventilation you can install sliding glass that can be opened and closed as necessary, but do remember not to leave the windows open at night.

• Nest boxes should be installed along the walls of the darkest part of the coop. It is best to fit the nest boxes with hinged roofs so that you can collect the eggs directly from the outside without needing to enter the coop itself.

• Fence the area of your garden or yard that you wish your chickens to live in with wire mesh or other fencing. Fences should be around 1.2 m (4 ft) high in order to keep predators out and chickens in.

• If you live in a location where birds of prey could be potential predators, cover the top of the coop with netting.

• Hang the feeders and waterers above the ground at a height where the tray is level with the chickens' backs so that it doesn't get dirty.

PART 5

YOUR FIRST LAYERS

MAKING YOUR CHICKENS COMFORTABLE

CHOOSING A COOP

Looking after chickens is basically a matter of common sense, but there are a few factors that need to be taken into account in order to raise the best chickens possible. These are good-quality feed, a clean living environment free from harmful diseases and also living conditions that are ideally free-range, or at least protected from predators such as foxes.

Providing a safe and secure coop for your chickens to live in is one of the most important things you must do. It needs to be of an adequate size for the number of hens you intend to keep, as well as having clean nesting and feeding areas.

If making a coop from scratch (see pages 54–56) seems a bit daunting, there are other, simpler DIY options and also reasonably priced shop-bought versions that might be right for you. You could perhaps even adapt an old rabbit hutch, unused shed or dog kennel.

The main points to take into account when making or purchasing a coop are as follows:

- The coop must be easy to clean, with good drainage.
- It should protect your birds against severe weather conditions whether that be the heat, cold, rain or wind, and keep out rodents, wild birds and predators.
- It should maintain a constant temperature, be free from draughts but also have good ventilation.
- The coop must have sufficient light coming in as

well as a proper feeding and watering area.

- The nesting area should be comfortable and tucked away from the main coop so the hens can lay their eggs in peace.

Once you have a fully-functioning chicken coop, whether it is home-made or shop-bought, it will be home to your chickens for the rest of their lives. Therefore, it is important that the coop is a comfortable and safe place for your chickens to eat, roost, lay and, if required, breed.

Floor space is the first thing to get right when making or purchasing your coop, and when deciding on these measurements you need to think not only of how many chickens you have now, but also whether you are going to increase your flock in the future. An adult chicken of medium size should have approximately 65 x 65 cm

HEN HINTS – EGG EATING

Egg eating is not a natural trait in chickens. It is usually caused by poor husbandry and maintenance of a flock. Egg breakage is one of the main causes, so ensuring that your chickens are getting enough of the right nutrients to produce strong shells and also that they are laying on to the right type of surface should help stop this. Finally, make sure that you collect the eggs early. Most hens have laid their eggs by 10am. If left all day the eggs are more likely to get damaged, resulting in the hens getting a taste of raw egg and thus developing the habit of eating them.

(2 x 2 ft) of space. If you don't give your birds enough space in their coop, you may as well be purchasing battery-farmed eggs from a supermarket.

HOME TO ROOST

Chickens, like the majority
of birds, will wish to roost
above the ground. If no
perches are available in the
coop the chickens will find
something else to sleep on
such as the feeder or nesting
box, which are not ideal.
Worse still, they may be
inclined to stay outside
if there are any perch-like
objects available in the
garden, which brings the
possibility of their making
a passing fox's evening a
much pleasanter one.

Nesting boxes (see pages
62–63 on how to make your
own) are another important

HEN HINTS – HANDLING

It is important to handle
chickens in a way that does
not make them uncomfortable
or frightened. Here are some
hen handling tips:

1. Approach the hen slowly.
2. Talk to it calmly and softly
   as you approach.
3. Slip one hand under the
   bird and hold it firmly by
   its legs.
4. Place the other hand on its
   back in order to restrain
   its wings.
5. Hold the bird close to your
   body and keep reassuring
   it throughout.

When handled in this way
the bird will be supported
securely and any risk of
damaging its wings will
be minimized.

factor in creating the perfect chicken coop for your birds. In relatively small coops, like most backyard ones tend to be, nesting boxes should be placed lower than the perches but above the ground as you want to discourage your chickens from laying their eggs on the floor. They should also be in the darkest area of the coop as this will encourage egg laying and also deter egg eating.

BRINGING CHICKENS HOME

If you have bought your chickens as pullets or youngsters, as opposed to rearing them from eggs, they could suffer from stress for the first couple of days. Experiencing the journey from their old home to the new one and finding themselves in an unfamiliar coop, potentially with other chickens they do not yet know, can cause chickens to become nervous. Allow them to get used to their new home and check on them from time to time to ensure they are settling in well to their new environment. If they do seem stressed, be patient with them, talk to them calmly and handle them slowly and gently.

ROUTINE

Chickens are creatures of habit, so it is best to introduce them gradually to the free-range life in your garden as opposed to letting them run wild from day one and then wondering why they do not roost where you want them to when evening comes. Keep them in the coop for the first couple of days and then confine them to a run for the rest of the first week. This will give them a chance to acclimatize to their new outdoor home. It should then be fine to let your chickens wander more freely as once they are in a routine they will know where to go as evening approaches.

MAKING A NESTING BOX

Chickens love the freedom to roam as they wish – pecking around your garden will be their favourite pastime. They also like space for roosting and can become stressed if confined either by other birds or by the size of the coop – but even though your hens need their space, they are social animals that like being part of a flock and it is important to get the balance right.

However, there is one area of their life where they like to be in a small, enclosed, cool (but not cold) and dark area, and that is when they lay their eggs.

Nesting boxes are an important part of the housing you create for your birds, as not only do they provide your hens with a laying sanctuary, they also make the job of egg collection much easier for you.

Opposite are some plans for a basic wooden nesting box that is made as an additional area to your main coop, but still adjoined. It is designed to be attached to a coop frame (see page 55 for an example plan) prior to the wall cladding being attached.

If this is too complex you can always purchase a nest box that can be attached to the inside of your coop.

However, nest boxes, whether home-made or bought from a supplier, can sometimes be a waste of time, as hens that have a lot of freedom may end up laying their eggs in all sorts of places. They may find somewhere in your garden, for example, that is more inviting than the nesting box you have provided for them.

Storage area

View from above

Perch

Nest   Nest   Nest

Front view

Lid to nestbox, providing access from outside the coop

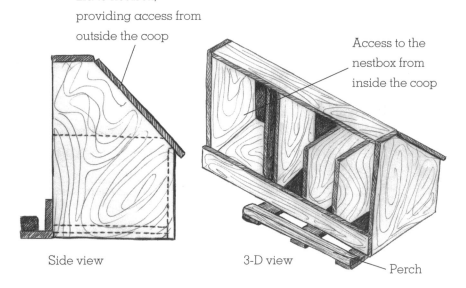

Access to the nestbox from inside the coop

Side view

3-D view

Perch

THE IMPORTANCE OF LIGHTING

Both daylight and darkness play important roles in good egg production. The hormones that control a hen's egg-laying cycle rely on the amount of light she has the benefit of on a daily basis. In the autumn, as daylight shortens, egg production will also start to decline (although some breeds will continue laying).

To encourage the longest possible season of egg-laying, bigger coops may have large windows installed in order for the hens to get the maximum amount of daylight. Coops may also be painted white on the inside to reflect what light is available.

Your birds need to be exposed to around 16 hours of light a day in order for them to continue to lay throughout the year. In smaller backyard coops, it may be necessary to provide extra artificial light from autumn to early spring. The job of the artificial light is not only to increase the length of the daylight available but also to provide a greater intensity which can sometimes be missing from autumn and winter days. Light intensity is measured with a light meter.

The best time to start providing artificial light is when your hens have finished growing their feathers after the autumn moult. In small coops a standard light bulb of 25-watts should be adequate, and if there is no electricity supply near the coop, a portable system using a 12-volt car battery will work perfectly.

Start with 60 minutes of extra light a day, gradually increasing by 30 minutes a week as the days get shorter. If you are able to fix a timer on your light, set it to come on before dawn rather than extending the light at the other end of the day. This means that your hens will not be caught out by a sudden fall of darkness in the afternoon before they have had a chance to get on to their perches to roost.

The light should be intense enough to be able to see your hens clearly at the feeder. The colour of the light you use is also important – it should be white to orange/yellow. Normal household energy-efficient bulbs or halogen lights are perfect.

HEN HINTS – LIGHTING

• Do not provide light to pullets before they have grown sufficiently as this will cause them to lay early and the eggs will be very small. The golden rule is: never increase light when birds are growing and never decrease light on mature layers.

• Increase the light gradually to a maximum of 16 hours including the natural daylight hours. Remember, hens need their sleep too!

• Do not allow the amount of light to shorten once your birds have started to lay.

FEEDING YOUR CHICKENS

Providing the right amount of the right feed to your chickens is important throughout their lives, but especially when they are at point of lay or fully-fledged layers. As is the case with most living creatures, food gives chickens the energy required to sustain life, helps them to maintain a well-functioning metabolism and keeps their immune system healthy.

Another important factor is that egg laying depletes their stores of energy, so they need to be fed regularly in order to lay on a near-daily basis.

As discussed on pages 48–50, the food you give them needs to be varied and balanced to provide them with the necessary nutrients not only to keep healthy themselves but also to produce good-quality eggs and,

potentially, healthy offspring. Manufactured feeds should provide your hens with the complete balance they require, in most cases without the need for any additional vitamins.

It is important to supply your hens with enough feeding space so that they can all feed at the same time. If your feeding area is too small, there may be a weaker bird or two who regularly misses out on her food. It is also easier, and better, if food is available to your hens constantly. Giving them food at set meal times, like you would a dog or a cat, can reduce productivity as there is more room for error. Do not worry about your hens overfeeding – they will simply stop eating when they have had sufficient for their needs.

FEED MANAGEMENT

It is important that the food you give your chickens is fresh and free from bacteria. Therefore, even if you decide to have food available for your chickens at all times as opposed to feeding them at intervals, it is sensible to limit the amount of food in the feeders so that the cycle of new food is regular. Refill your feeders first thing in the morning and then check throughout the day, replenishing whenever stocks become depleted. If there is any leftover food in the feeders at the end of the day it should be removed prior to refilling the next morning.

Outside or inside the coop

Where you provide the feed is really up to you. Some people prefer to have their feeders separate from the coop so that their hens are eating outside and away from where they roost and nest.

However, if you follow this line of reasoning it is important to put the food out of reach of predators and vermin. The last thing you want is to entice a family of rats into your garden for lunch.

Manufactured layer feeds

A layer feed should be used if your chickens are laying eggs for your consumption. Such feeds contain about 16 per cent protein, plus additional calcium in order to ensure strong eggshells. Start using this feed either when your bird reaches 20 weeks, or when she lays her first egg – whichever comes first.

Scratch

Hens need (and love) to scratch. They do this by using their feet to turn over the ground in order to find seeds, grit, insects or plants to eat. Supplying your hens with 'scratch grains' will help to stimulate this natural trait, alleviate boredom and give them exercise. However, if you are feeding your hens a complete manufactured diet, scratches should be used sparingly as they can potentially dilute the nutrients found in the feed. Try to limit their scratch intake to either about 10 per cent of their daily food intake, or no more than can be eaten in 20 minutes.

Grit

If you do decide to supply your hens with scratch, ensure that they have an insoluble grit available to help break down the grains. If your hens have access to soil, they will find enough in the form of grit and pebbles. If they are kept on grass you may have to purchase a bag of grit and sprinkle it over the ground around their coop.

Scraps from the home

Chickens enjoy scraps from the kitchen table, especially greens. But, as in the case of scratch, if you are feeding your hens a manufactured layer feed, make sure you do not overfeed them with these tasty extras as it can have a detrimental effect on their egg productivity. A few scraps are fine, and dark leafy greens will help your hens produce eggs with a rich orange yolk as opposed to the insipid yellow yolks often associated with supermarket eggs.

Manufactured feed versus home-mixed feed

Ready-mixed feeds provide hens with the correct balance of nutrients to suit each stage of their lives. Nevertheless, backyard keepers may find that the costs involved in using this feed are rather high, and may even counteract the thrifty spirit of keeping hens in the first place.

Another concern is that many manufactured feeds contain antibiotics. Although

The following is a guide to the basic starter, grower and layer home mixes which should be combined to make 45 kg/ 99 lb).

	45 kg (99 lb) of mix					
	Starter		**Grower**		**Layer**	
Coarsely ground grain (corn, milo, barley, oats, wheat, rice, etc.)	kg	lb	kg	lb	kg	lb
	21	46	22.5	49½	24	53
Wheat bran, mill feed, rice bran, milling by-products etc.	4.5	10	8	17½	7.5	16½
Soybean meal	13	28¾	7.5	16½	7	15
Meat meal, fish meal (soybean meal may be substituted for either of these)	2.2	5	2.2	5	1.3	2¾
Alfalfa meal (can be left out if fresh pasture is available)	1.8	4	1.8	4	1.8	4
Yeast, milk powder (can be left out if vitamin supplement is properly balanced)	0.9	2	0.9	2	0.9	2
Salt with trace minerals (Trace mineral salt or iodized salt supplemented with 14 g of manganese sulphage and 14 g of zinc oxide)	0.225	½	0.225	½	0.225	½
Bone meal, deflourinated dicalcium phosphate	0.9	2	0.9	2	0.9	2
Ground limestone, oyster shells	0.5	1	0.9	2	1.3	2¾

this is obviously helpful if your hen has an illness, if she does not, feeding her with unnecessary medication goes against the natural approach that most smallholders are trying to achieve.

If you decide not to purchase chicken feed for your laying hens, ensuring that they receive the balanced diet they require is down to you. Manufactured feed may be better in the first 8–10 weeks of a chick's life but as they get older, a more natural method is easier to sustain.

Mixing your own feed can be satisfying and you are able to control exactly which ingredients go into it, making it as organic and natural as you wish.

SUPPLEMENTARY MASH

If you decide on a home-made mix, supplementing it with mashes made from household scraps is a good way of giving your chickens a more balanced and well-rounded diet. Home-made mashes are also an excellent way of using up left-over household vegetables that may otherwise go to waste.

All you need to do is add any left-over vegetables (ideally root and leafy green ones) to a pot of boiled water and gently simmer until the vegetables soften and become a heavy mash. Use only the amount of water that the vegetables are capable of absorbing as you do not want the finished mixture to be too moist.

In addition to vegetables, you can also add leftover bread, cake, biscuits, pasta, rice or old breakfast cereals to the mash. Do be sensible with cake and biscuit products, though – for chickens as well as for their keepers, these items should be enjoyed only in moderation! It is not a good idea for chickens to have too much sugar in their diet.

BROODY HENS – TROUBLESHOOTING

Broodiness is an instinctive behaviour in female animals, and chickens are no exception. Consequently, a broody hen is something that all chicken keepers will have to contend with at some point.

A hen will have the instinctive urge to sit on her eggs and incubate them for the 21 days it takes them to hatch, and most hens will follow this instinct two to three times a year, especially in spring and summer.

Obviously, allowing your hen to go broody means that she will not be producing any eggs for you to eat for about three weeks. Therefore, if you want maximum egg production from your flock, you will need to be able to recognize the signs and take avoiding action.

WHAT TO LOOK FOR

- A hen that happily stays in the nest box for most of the day and night.

- Fluffing of feathers and a protective guttural squawk if you approach.

- A new anxiety and aggression; attempts at pecking anyone who goes near her nest.

- Speedy eating – a broody hen will run quickly to the feeder, eat, and possibly take a quick dust bath (see page 75) before returning to the nest.

- Plucking of feathers from her underside. This is to allow her body heat to reach the eggs.

Although broodiness is natural, it can be harmful not only to the broody hen but also to the rest of the flock. Broody hens are more likely to neglect themselves as all their effort is concentrated on incubating their eggs. As a result of not grooming or eating properly and lack of movement from sitting on the eggs for such long periods of time they become more likely to suffer from parasitic infections. These are more rife in the warmer months and this coincides with the time when hens are more prone to broodiness.

A broody hen can also upset the rest of your flock if you have only limited space with a single nest box. If the nest is constantly occupied by a broody hen the others have nowhere to lay their eggs, and it can cause bullying. Also, the nest box will become a lot dirtier than usual and the calm state of a happy hen house will be disrupted.

DISCOURAGING BROODINESS

- Remove eggs regularly from the nest box so hens do not have a chance to get attached to their lay.

- If you notice a hen going broody encourage her outside the coop by picking her up and placing her outside with the others.

- If she constantly returns to the nest box, blocking it off may be necessary.

- If the signs are still there, removing the broody hen from the rest of the flock and transferring her to a cooler place, such as a crate in the garage, should help to distract her from the need to sit on her eggs.

- Act fast – the longer you leave a hen brooding the longer it will take to break the habit.

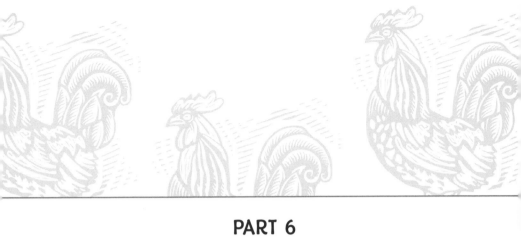

PART 6

CARING FOR YOUR LAYERS

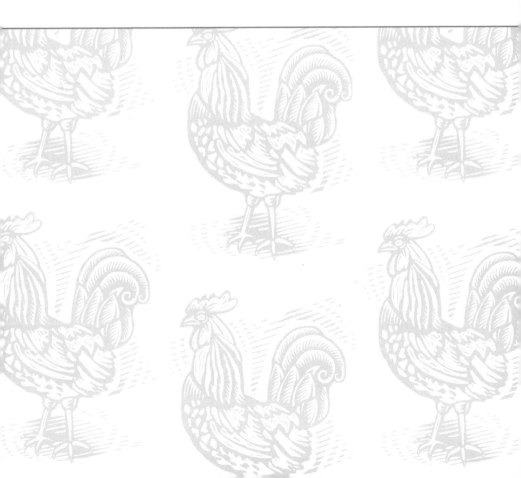

MAINTAINING YOUR FLOCK

Hens are easy animals to keep, but they still need a fair amount of looking after. It is a good idea to read the daily, weekly and monthly tasks listed below to assess whether your lifestyle can accommodate their needs, or if you are willing to change your routine if necessary.

DAILY TASK CHECK LIST

• Ensure that the hens' run is closed correctly and open the pop-hole of the coop.

• Check that each bird looks fit and well and is not showing any signs of abnormal behaviour.

• Replenish food stores.

• Check that there is enough grit available.

• Make sure the water vessel is clean and replenish with fresh water.

• Collect the eggs – it is worth checking for eggs again later in the day if not all hens have laid by the time of the first check.

• Make sure that there is enough dust in the dust-box (see opposite).

• Once eggs have been collected, check the nest boxes and replace any soiled bedding with fresh.

• If it has been raining check the ground for puddles. If there is grass where your birds range, make more holes with a fork to increase drainage. Chickens must be discouraged from drinking muddy water as it increases the risk of them getting parasites.

• Near sundown, check that all birds are safely back inside the coop and close the pop-hole.

Between the morning and the late afternoon or early evening, hens can be left alone to follow their own daily routine, which will mostly involve pecking, sheltering from the sun, eating and drinking.

WEEKLY TASKS

In a 'deep littering' system, the litter is covered with fresh straw on a weekly basis so that over the winter, layers of rotting straw covered by

HEN HINT – DUST BATHS

Chickens don't use water to wash, but bathing in dust is an important part of their routine. The dust helps to keep their feathers in good condition by soaking up excess oils and moisture. Dust baths are also a way for chickens to get rid of any parasites that might infest their feathers, and in the summer they play a part in keeping the birds cool.

If you do not have much soil available in your back garden for them to wallow in, you can make a simple dust bath by placing a wooden or plastic box measuring approximately 30 × 55 cm (12 × 22 in) and 20 cm (8 in) deep in the garden and filling it three-quarters full with soil. Keep it in a shaded area of the run or your free-range area, ensuring that it is cleaned out and replenished regularly. If you do keep it outside, you may wish to move it into the coop in heavy rain so that it does not become a mud bath.

new straw are built up. In the spring it is all removed and composted (making a great growing medium for mushrooms) and the process begins again. However, deep littering is not so acceptable in an urban environment or a garden or yard lacking in space. First, neighbours in close proximity would probably not thank you for the smell it produces and secondly, the smell would potentially bring rats to investigate – something your neighbours would hate even more.

So if you live in an urban area it is best to clean your coop on a weekly basis instead. Wear sturdy gloves when cleaning out the coop and wash your hands immediately afterwards.

WEEKLY TASK CHECK LIST

• Remove the droppings board or liner and add the droppings to your compost heap. Do not let your chickens have access to the compost.

• Clean the board or replace the liner.

• Brush out the coop and wipe down the perches.

• Check the coop for any signs of intrusion such as holes, scratches, gnaw marks or even blood marks.

• Check the birds for signs of mites by looking underneath their wings, vents and necks.

• Look for signs of scaly leg, caused by a burrowing mite leaving crusty deposits that push the scales outwards.

MONTHLY TASKS

The bigger husbandry tasks need doing less often, but make sure you note down when they are due to be done as forgetting them could mark the end of your flock.

MONTHLY TASK CHECK LIST

• Chickens need to be wormed on a monthly basis – do this by adding the anti-worming preparation to their food or water, making sure you follow the manufacturer's instructions.

• It may be worth treating your flock for mites and lice as a preventative measure even if you have not actually seen any. You will be able to purchase preventative medications online, from your local poultry supplier or even from larger pet shops and hardware shops.

• Every month, disinfect the surfaces of your hen coop and nesting box in addition to the usual weekly clean.

• Check the condition of the hen coop, nesting box and run and make any repairs as necessary. Keeping on top of these tasks can save money, time and even your birds' lives.

HEN HINT

If you have sufficient room, it is a good idea to periodically move the coop and run to an area of fresh soil or grass. You do not have to move them far – just so that there is new soil underneath the coop. Soil can get contaminated over time, so this will help to stop the spread of anything untoward and also give the old soil time to rejuvenate. If you do not have room to do this, or the site of your chicken coop and run is fixed, then a removable solid floor that can be taken out and cleaned regularly would be best.

WING CLIPPING

Wing clipping is the most common way of keeping chickens within the boundaries that have been allocated to them. Even though chickens cannot fly as well as most other birds, they are still able to reach enough height to get to places you would rather they did not, especially if you are keeping them free-range.

If your birds do have a tendency to take off they can put themselves in danger from predators or, in urban areas, busy roads. Prevention by wing clipping is the best way to deal with this. Clipping the first six flight feathers of just one of your bird's wings will cause her to lose the balance required to fly – be sure that you do not clip both wings, or you will restore her balance and unless she is a heavy bird she will still

be able to fly, albeit with more effort.

Before you proceed with clipping your chickens' wings, assess first whether it really is a necessity. Not all birds have the urge to leave the area allocated to them, so watch your flock for a few days first and gauge their behaviour. Although clipping should not hurt a bird it can cause them to panic, the stress of which could lead to decreased egg production for a while, so it is worth checking whether it is definitely required before going ahead.

Wing clipping needs to be done annually, since the flight feathers will grow back after the autumn moult. If you have someone to assist you with wing clipping it will make the task easier – one of you can hold the bird while the other does the clipping.

HOW TO CLIP

The following instructions will make wing clipping painless and stress-free for your flock :

- Take hold of your hen gently (see page 60) and wrap her in an old towel with one wing exposed. Turn her upside down. This has an immediate calming effect as it puts the bird in a sort of trance, making them docile.

- Keep talking to her gently as it will be much easier to clip her wing if she feels safe and calm.

- Spread out the exposed wing completely in order to locate the flight feathers, which are nearest to the tip of the wing. They are longer than the rest of the wing feathers and, more often than not, a different colour.

- It is extremely important that you do not cut any new growth feathers, as it will cause pain to your bird and serious, sometimes fatal, blood-loss. You can recognize new growth feathers as they will still have blood in the shaft (quill) so will have a red or pink tone. On some darker-coloured birds you may have to hold the wing up to the sun or a bright light in order to identify this.

- Once you have located the correct feathers to clip, take a large pair of sharp scissors with rounded ends and cut six feathers approximately one third of the way down. You can do this in stages, clipping a little off at a time, if you are worried about taking off too much.

- When you have finished clipping the wing, make sure you put the scissors a safe distance away and gently release the bird.

THE PECKING ORDER

Even if you have the healthiest, extremely well looked after birds, they will still come up against behavioural problems due to the natural characteristics of the species. This is why it is important to spend time getting to know your flock and learning about their individual personalities and traits. That way, it will be easier to judge if you have a bully in your flock, or a weaker hen who could get 'pecked' on. Nevertheless, you will never be able to alter the natural hierarchy in your flock.

Like many creatures on this planet, chickens are a pack animal and within the flock there is a well-defined pecking order. Each bird plays an individual role in the flock, and each bird knows its place on the social ladder, easily dominating other birds that are of lower ranking.

There is always one bird that will come at the top of the flock, to whom all the others will show respect, mostly by staying out of their way! The top bird will show their status by making a low growling noise warning the other birds not to approach. They may also raise the feathers along their neck which is a sign of disapproval, or attack another bird lower down the social ladder if they step out of line.

Usually, the top bird would be a cock, but if there are no males around then the position would probably be held by one of the elder and usually larger hens. If this is the case and a young male is brought into the flock, she may still keep her position if he is not brave or mature enough to stand his ground. It is down to each bird to find its role in this social setup.

FEATHER PECKING

A problem that you may encounter among your flock is feather pecking, when a bird damages its own plumage by pecking at it repeatedly. This is not uncommon, and if a hen does this over a period of time she may peck the skin itself and end up drawing blood. This can make things much worse, as when the rest of your flock get the taste for blood they will join in and start pecking at the bird which began it all and then at each other.

However, feather pecking does not always start with an individual pecking herself; it can also be caused by the stronger birds in the flock – those higher in the pecking order – bullying the younger or weaker birds in the flock. Eventually this may lead to a full-blown case of chicken cannibalism and this is something to be avoided if at all possible.

CAUSES OF FEATHER PECKING

Overcrowding

Birds need their own space. Make sure that the coop and outside space they have to live, if not completely free-range, is of ample size. Allow at least 65 x 65 cm (2 x 2 ft) per chicken inside the coop with at least an additional 70 x 70 cm (2.5 x 2.5 ft) of space in their outside area. Obviously, the more space you can give them the better. Hens that get to spend their days outdoors are less likely to get into this habit.

It is worth also checking how the nest boxes are being used – you should have one nest box per 3–4 hens, but if they are aggravating one another it may be worth increasing this number.

Boredom

In a completely natural environment a chicken would spend a large part of its daily routine foraging for food. Domesticated chickens, however, with a well-balanced diet available to them from a human keeper, may well have reached their daily food requirements within a couple of hours. This means that they need to fill their day with other behavioural traits and pecking themselves or each other is a popular choice.

This can be minimized by spreading their feed around their outside area so that they have to put some effort into feeding, which will fill their time more safely. However, do ensure that there is enough food and water to go around – if they have to fight for every last grain they could make up for the shortfall by trying to eat one another.

CHICKEN CHAT

Can chickens change sex?

Although a chicken cannot literally change sex, they can switch their behaviour to act like the opposite sex. This can be due to a hormonal imbalance caused either by a disease or some form of injury to the ovaries.

For example, a hen might start growing spurs as well as cockerel feathers. She may also attempt to mate with other hens within the flock. These traits usually occur in a single-sex flock that does not have a real cockerel. This apparent cockerel cannot actually fertilize eggs – all she can do is take over the role of the male in the flock.

There have been occasional reports of hens that have become transgender, taking on the role of both hen and cockerel, but this is rare.

Poor nutrition

If your birds' feed is lacking in certain vitamins and nutrients essential to their well-being they may start to peck at their own or another hen's feathers in search of what they are lacking. Double check that what you are feeding them covers their nutritional daily requirements.

Feeding your flock with high-fibre diets and providing additional grain or straw in the litter during rearing could result in lower levels of feather pecking. Also, a study carried out in 2005 found that a low-energy diet could lengthen eating time by as much as 14 per cent by reducing the speed that the birds ate at, leaving less time, and energy, for feather pecking.

Cleanliness

Remember that it is important to keep on top of cleaning your coop, nest box and run. Badly maintained housing can result in an infestation of mites and lice. Hens will then peck at their feathers to relieve the itching. Ensure that the coop is cleaned every week and disinfect everything on a monthly basis.

Light

If hens are exposed to light that is too bright or shafts of bright light interspersed with dark areas it can cause them to become anxious and stressed. Even though hens need a good deal of light in order to stay healthy, they also need dark areas to relax and also lay in. Check that your hens are not getting any more than 16 hours of light a day, and also that it is not too intense. Make sure that the nest boxes are free from bright flashes of light at all times – they should be in the darkest area of the coop.

If you are using artificial light and think this may be the cause of the pecking, try changing your current bulb for one with a redder hue.

CURES AND RECOVERY

If feather pecking is already a problem and it is too late for the preventative methods mentioned, you will need to use the following procedures to get on top of the problem and hopefully cure it:

- Apply an unpleasant-tasting substance such as a strong mustard to the affected chickens.

- Pine tar can also be applied to the affected area as it is naturally germicidal and anti-bacterial. Its other benefit is that its thick, greasy texture will discourage birds from further pecking.

- Buying or making a cereal-based block for the chickens to peck at will alleviate boredom and help to occupy their pecking instinct.

- Any birds that are severely affected, especially ones that are bleeding, may need to be taken out of the main coop and put into isolation in order to aid their recovery. Do make sure that any birds that are isolated from the main flock still have the same standards of care and management.

- In order to assist your chickens' recovery feed them extra protein, such as mealworms, as this will help to stimulate new feather growth.

- If necessary you can trim your flock's beaks, which is done by removing the pointed tip of the upper beak. This will prevent feather pecking but it can also stop your hens from eating certain foods, so trimming should be a last resort. If it has to be done call in a professional to carry it out.

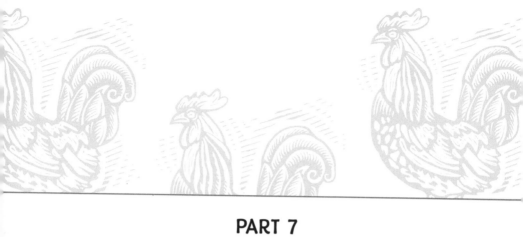

PART 7

A HEALTHY FLOCK

COMMON PROBLEMS

If you take good care of your flock, most problems associated with chickens and other poultry can be avoided. As long as you provide your birds with plenty of inside and outside space, sufficient light, protection from severe weather conditions and draughts, a balanced diet, fresh water and clean living conditions, cases of infirm birds should be minimal. However, even if you take maximum care over the hygiene, feeding and general maintenance of your birds there is still the possibility that diseases will occur.

The larger your flock, the more chance you have of encountering disease. The reason why a bird has fallen ill will often remain a mystery and the rest of your flock may remain unaffected. It is estimated that even the most perfectly maintained flock will lose approximately 5 per cent of its birds per year, for a number of reasons. The time for real concern is when two or three birds show signs of illness within the space of a couple of days.

No matter what the cause of illness, the sick bird (or birds) should be moved out of the main coop and isolated from the rest of the flock to help prevent a disease spreading if it turns out to be a contagious one. It will also prevent the feather pecking and cannibalism that may occur if the rest of the flock are disturbed by the presence of the sick bird.

DEALING WITH DISEASE

The most common diseases your chickens are likely to suffer from are of the respiratory kind. The symptoms you will notice a bird suffering from are much like the human symptoms of a common cold. Your hen may have a discharge of nasal mucus or blocked nostril holes. She may also sneeze and make coughing sounds, and be generally uninterested in her food or usual routine.

Most of the time these ailments will be minor and turn out to be a humdrum cold that will run its course just as they do in humans; the best medicine is just a little love and care. However, it is still important to keep a close eye on any poorly birds and not return them to the flock until you are confident they are better or know that they what they have is not contagious.

HEN HINTS

Always wash your hands thoroughly after handling any sick birds so that you do not risk spreading the problem to the rest of your flock. Also, do not feed your birds with any raw meat as this can cause toxoplasmosis, which can be transmitted to humans through contaminated chicken manure. Pregnant women and small children need to be especially careful to avoid coming into contact with any source of this.

CHICKEN DISEASES

The following is a list of ailments you may encounter when keeping chickens. Some of these diseases are more common and treatable than others, and in all cases the sooner you notice the problem, the more chance you have of your bird making a full recovery if the condition they have is treatable.

It is important to find an avian vet who specializes in poultry if possible, since many local veterinary practices that deal with domestic pets such as cats and dogs will not have the specialized knowledge that is required to treat your birds.

ASPERGILLOSIS

More commonly referred to as brooder pneumonia, aspergillosis is caused by the birds inhaling spores of fungus found on mouldy litter, food or nesting material. The typical symptoms of this disease are excessive thirst, quickness and shortness of breath, inflamed eyes and a slumped posture. Young birds are particularly at risk and although there is no cure, antibiotics have been known to help in mild cases. Aspergillosis can be avoided by sticking to a regular cleaning routine and making sure that litter is changed regularly and that any damp nesting material and feed are also replaced.

AVIAN INFLUENZA (BIRD FLU)

This is caused by various strains of virus and affects a bird's respiratory system. It will affect a chicken in much the same way influenza affects humans. You might notice that the bird's head and neck are slightly swollen, and usually there is a nasal

H5N1

H5N1 is a virus subtype of avian influenza and is a mutated virus that can pass from birds to humans. There have been recent outbreaks around the world where humans have come into contact with poultry infected with this disease and have become extremely ill, in some cases fatally so. Wild birds carry the H5N1 virus but are largely unaffected by it; the problem is that they can spread it to poultry flocks far away from the one where they picked it up. There is also a concern that the H5N1 strain will eventually become transmissable from human to human and could result in a deadly pandemic with terrible consequences for the human race.

It is very unlikely, especially in an urban situation, that any chickens you keep will become infected by this disease. The only possible route of infection as yet is from wild birds which are able to migrate from the Far East and this is extremely unlikely. However, it is something to be aware of. You may not be able to tell that your birds are infected – they will simply die. If you do have any sudden deaths in your flock it is a good idea to have a post-mortem carried out to discern the cause. Also, ensure that you do not handle any potentially infected birds without being covered up and do not bring them into your home.

discharge. Birds may also appear depressed, lose their appetite and cease producing eggs. It is a contagious disease with two main forms. The first is 'low pathogenic', which causes only mild symptoms and may even go undetected, while the second is 'highly pathogenic' and spreads rapidly through poultry flocks; it can shut down the bird's major organs within the space of 48 hours. There is no treatment available for either of these strains but the mortality rate is low in the mild form if you have a fit and healthy flock. However, in the highly pathogenic strain the mortality rate can be as high as 100 per cent.

It is vital to remove any birds suspected of having this disease from the rest of the flock as quickly as possible so that the spread of the virus is minimized. The incubation periods for avian influenza can vary from just a few hours to three days in individual birds and up to 14 days to spread throughout a flock.

AVIAN TUBERCULOSIS

This chronic wasting disease is caused by a bacterial infection. Birds infected with tuberculosis often appear weak and gaunt, with possible lameness. They may also suffer from diarrhoea and have an unkempt appearance, with scraggy feathers and weak legs. All species of birds are prone to this disease but it is domestic poultry that are most commonly affected, especially the older birds within a flock.

Avian tuberculosis is contagious and will spread through an entire flock. This disease can also be transmitted from one species to another, so if you keep other animals and suspect your flock may be infected, separate your animals from each other. There is no cure for this illness and you may even be required to cull your entire flock to avoid further spread.

BUMBLE FOOT

This is the common name for a swelling which is the result of a cut or graze on the underside of the bird's foot that has become infected. The wound heals on the outside but leaves a solid piece of pus on the inside, which makes the bird limp. It is usually caused by jumping from a perch that is too high or scratching about on sharp, flinty ground.

If you look at your affected bird's foot you will notice a hard abscess and by applying some pressure you may find it possible to burst it. However, it may require lancing with a sterilized blade. Either way, after the pus has been released an antiseptic ointment or hydrogen peroxide should be applied to the area. It is best to keep the affected bird away from the rest of the flock, in a pen with a flooring of clean straw, for a few days until it heals.

CORYZA

This highly infectious disease caused by the bacterium *Haemophilus paragallinarum* is characterized by a mucusy inflammation of the upper respiratory tract. Other symptoms include facial swelling, loss of appetite, nasal discharge and a drop in egg production.

The mortality rate in cases of coryza is low and sulphur drugs added to the feed or water should combat it within a couple of weeks if there are no complications. However, culling may be needed in severe cases if birds show symptoms of head swelling.

EGG BINDING

This is the term for a hen being unable to lay an egg which has been formed. There can be several reasons for this and it should be treated by an avian vet immediately. Symptoms that indicate your hen is egg-bound are that she will sit on the floor for long periods of time and strain excessively; she will also have a swollen area around her vent and her droppings will increase in size. It is a serious condition that can result in death if not treated immediately. You can ease your hen's discomfort while waiting for the vet to arrive by attaching a heat mat to one half of the underside of a cage to create a heat gradient. This will help the bird's oviduct wall to contract. It is, however, imperative that you do not overheat or burn your hen.

EGG DROP SYNDROME

Originally a condition prevalent in ducks and geese, EDS is now a problem in chickens of all ages, especially broilers and breeds that lay brown eggs. It is an infectious disease caused by a virus and is characterized by eggs with thin shells, or no shells at all. As infected birds can spread the disease through their droppings, keeping a clean coop and outside area is crucial in stopping its spread. Although it can have an adverse effect on egg production, the birds themselves will remain healthy and after approximately four weeks should revert back to normal laying. There is no treatment for EDS, but vaccination at the point of lay will provide protection.

FOWL POX

Also known as bird pox and avian diphtheria, fowl pox can affect chickens regardless of their age or breed. It is transmitted via mosquitoes, infected food and water and contact with other infected birds. It comes in two forms, wet and dry. The former causes lesions that have a fungal-like appearance and can be found on the bird's mouth, pharynx, larynx and trachea, while the latter has wart-like characteristics that form on unfeathered areas of the bird. Symptoms that may appear before the lesions themselves are retarded growth in young birds, a weak appearance and a decline in egg production.

The dry lesions are uncomfortable for your bird rather than anything to really worry about and will take approximately two weeks to heal. The wet lesions, however, are more serious as they can obstruct the bird's air passage, causing breathing problems. There is no treatment for fowl pox and vaccination is the only way to deal with this condition. If you suspect your bird already has fowl pox – and if you have caught it early enough – vaccination can still work.

INFECTIOUS BRONCHITIS

This disease is highly contagious and spreads by the air and by infected birds, coops, feeders and even rodents. It will sweep rapidly throughout a flock. Symptoms include a decline in feeding and drinking, shivering, persistent chirping, a watery discharge in the eyes and nostrils, inflammation of the eyes and possible signs of breathing difficulties caused by a build-up of a cheese-like substance in the windpipe. Bronchitis will also cause poor egg production.

Cleanliness, the strength of your birds' immune systems, the presence of other diseases and the age of your birds are all factors that can affect the severity of an episode of bronchitis. There are no specific treatments, but a course of antibiotics will help to lessen any secondary complications that may arise from it. The best way to manage this virus is to increase the room temperature for any sick birds and also maintain a good hygiene level. Mortality rate in chicks can be as high as 60 per cent but in fully-grown birds it is only 2 per cent. There are vaccines available that can be provided if there has been an outbreak of great concern in your local area.

INTERNAL AND EXTERNAL PARASITES

There are many types of worm and mite that can affect your flock, and many of them are hard to eliminate completely. The best way to keep your chickens free from such parasites is to treat them with worming powders and mite repellents before you think they may actually be afflicted. Good coop and feed cleanliness as well as regular ground rotation if this is possible are key in curbing the build-up of such infestations.

HEN HINT – ANTIBIOTICS

If you need to use antibiotics on your hens it is best not to eat the meat or eggs they produce while they are being treated or for a period of time afterwards, while the drug is still in their bodies. Check the label to see how long it takes for the antibiotic to leave the system.

Antibiotics are used regularly in commercial poultry farms not only to fight infection but also to stimulate growth. Some antibiotics are similar to medicines used for human consumption and there is concern that eating eggs and chickens containing residues of these drugs may, in the long-term, make humans immune to the drug, thus making us unable to fight disease. Occasional employment of antibiotics on your home-reared birds will not cause any problems, but use them sparingly.

Gapeworms

In gapeworm, the windpipe of the bird becomes blocked by a parasitic worm called *Syngamus trachea*. The worms are transmitted to chickens via contaminated soil or food, including earthworms, and become embedded in their lungs and windpipe. A regular poultry wormer is the best treatment; if your birds are free-range, ensure that the area they are on is rotated regularly so that the parasites do not build up. **Symptoms:** Repeated opening of beak and soundless gaping. The bird may also have shortness of breath, trouble feeding and a loss of appetite, which can result in listlessness.

Capillaria worms (Hair worms)

These thin worms up to 2 cm (¾ in) long can use earthworms as an intermediate host, growing into adults once your bird has eaten the infected earthworm. They will live in the upper part of the chicken's digestive system.
Symptoms: Pale green diarrhoea, pale egg yolks, hunched bodies and sagging wings. Severe infestation can result in death.

Roundworms

Even though chickens can put up with a certain amount of roundworms in their system these can build up to an intolerable level in unclean conditions. Make sure that droppings are not left to build up; moving birds on to clean ground will help.
Symptoms: Loss of condition, poor growth, listlessness, diarrhoea and pale egg yolks.

Tapeworms

It is very difficult to prevent an occurrence of tapeworms as they are carried in larvae form by many insects that will become part of your chickens' diet. Once in the birds' intestines, the larvae will develop into adult worms, growing to about 10 cm (4 in) long. They will not cause any problems unless left to build up. Regular worming of your birds is essential.

Symptoms: A drop in egg production, increase in hunger and possible diarrhoea.

Lice

These small greyish brown insects live on the bird's body and feed off blood, dead skin and feather roots. They will be found mostly on the rear of the bird, especially around the vent area. Louse powder is the most effective treatment and should be applied once every four days for a fortnight; put some in the dust bath and treat the coop, nest box and perches too. If you suspect a severe outbreak of lice in your flock it may be worth moving them into a temporary home while the coop is professionally fumigated.

Symptoms: Parting the hen's feathers will show small grey-brown parasites scuttling across the body. They can cause severe irritation that will result in the hen pecking at its feathers and skin to relieve the sensation, causing sores and general depression.

Red mite

This is one of the most common mites that affects poultry and although they are grey in colour, once they have fed on the bird's blood they turn red, hence their name. They hide in the corners of the coop and wait until night time when the chickens are roosting to attack.

Symptoms: Pale combs and wattles, decreased appetite, low or nil egg production and an unwillingness to roost in the coop at night are all signs of red mite. The coop may smell musty and have a layer of white dust. You may notice small bugs that can cause skin irritation.

PART 8

YOUR FIRST EDIBLE EGGS

YOUR FIRST EGGS

Once your hens are fully grown, at home in their coop, feeding well and with enough light to stimulate egg production, they will then be ready to lay. One of the first signs that a chicken is about to lay is a continual moaning noise much like the typical 'clucking' sound associated with hens. She will also start walking to and from her nesting box before finally settling there.

The early eggs will be smaller than the eggs your hen will lay in the future, and the first one may be imperfect – it could even lack a yolk. This is common in the first few lays and nothing to worry about; it can take a hen a while to start laying perfect eggs.

Once she has laid her egg your hen will let everyone around her know by cackling loudly. Even though the first eggs will be small and may not be fully formed, collect them from her otherwise she may go broody. Be patient, ensure that your bird has all her needs met and within a couple of months at the latest she will start to lay perfectly formed eggs of a decent size for her breed. A healthy hen will produce between 150 and 250 eggs a year, depending upon the breed. This number can be increased to see you through the winter months if you decide to use artificial lighting (see pages 64–65 for more information).

ROUTINE, ROUTINE AND MORE ROUTINE

The most important thing, as with everything in chicken keeping, is getting your hens into a routine. You can encourage them to lay their eggs in the nest boxes rather than on the floor by placing artificial eggs, or even golf balls, in the nest boxes and making sure that the nest boxes are comfortably lined with wood shavings or straw as this will make them more enticing. If you do spot any eggs on the floor, get rid of them immediately so that your birds do not think that this is the acceptable place for them to lay.

Even though hens do not like to lay their eggs at night and will hold on to an egg until morning before releasing it, they do like a dark area to do their laying in. Therefore, it is important that the nest box is in the darkest area of the coop.

CHICKEN CHAT

As a very general rule, hens with white ear lobes lay white eggs and those with red ear lobes lay brown eggs. There are, however, exceptions to the rule such as the Araucana, which has bright red ear lobes but lays eggs that are blueish in colour, and the Dorking, which has red ear lobes but lays white eggs. Asiatic breeds tend to lay brown eggs whereas the Mediterranean breeds lay white eggs.

COLLECTING YOUR EGGS

It is hard to estimate exactly when your hens are going to lay their eggs. Morning is a good time to go and inspect the coop for them. There is an interval of 25–26 hours from one egg being laid to the next, so as the week goes on, whatever time the hen laid her first egg, the next one will be approximately an hour later each day. On this basis, as hens do not lay at night, there will probably be a day or two every couple of weeks when your hen takes a break and does not lay.

You should collect your eggs often. Two to three times a day is preferable, so if you work you should check for eggs before you leave in the morning, upon your return, and before the hens roost for the night. The main reason for regular egg collection is damage limitation. The longer the eggs are left, the higher the chance of them being broken by unruly claws and beaks, which could lead to your chicken getting a taste for the yolk (see below).

As you collect the eggs, place them gently in a container where they will not roll into one another. You can purchase cardboard egg boxes for storing your eggs from your local farm or hatchery. Using a pencil, lightly write the date of collection on each egg so that you use the older eggs first.

HEN HINT

If one of your hens does start eating eggs, a good way to put a stop to it is by making a small hole at the top and bottom of a couple of eggs and blowing out the contents. Then fill up the empty shells with mustard and entice the miscreant hen into eating them. After a couple of pecks at the mustard-eggs the problem should be solved.

STORING EGGS

When you collect your eggs you may notice that some of them are a little dirty. If you were to wash them on collection you would remove the protective membrane called the bloom that stops infections getting through the porous shell. Not only is this coating a form of protection if the egg is fertilized, it also helps to preserve the egg when you are storing it to eat. If it were gone, the egg would need to be consumed within a few days as it would no longer be protected from airborne bacteria. In contrast, an unwashed egg that has not received much handling and has been promptly placed in the refrigerator will stay fresh for up to six months or more. Eggs do not have to be stored in a refrigerator but it prolongs their life somewhat.

For long-life eggs, follow these tips for keeping them as fresh as possible:

- If the egg is not soiled with any manure or mud, gently brush off any loose dust and put the egg straight into the refrigerator without rinsing it first.

- Take care not to over-handle your eggs as this can wear away the bloom.

- If the egg is slightly soiled it may be possible to flick off the dirt with your nail. If that does not work, gently rub the soiled area with a very fine sandpaper. Remember that this may compromise the bloom, so it is best to use eggs such as these sooner rather than later.

- If an egg is heavily soiled it must be washed prior to storing. Chicken manure harbours the harmful bacteria salmonella and putting soiled eggs straight into a refrigerator with other food could spread this. Again, as the bloom has been compromised you should use up these eggs first. Make sure you wash your hands and disinfect whatever you have used to remove the dirt to avoid contamination of other food.

- If boiling, run eggs under cool water first to remove the bloom. If any dirt or bacteria is stuck to the shell it could be absorbed during cooking.

- Do not soak your eggs in water to clean. You will be removing the bloom and then your eggs will be left in a bowl of dirty water which can then infiltrate through the shell and contaminate the egg inside.

- If any dirty eggs are even slightly cracked it is best not to use them as the contents may be infected with bacteria.

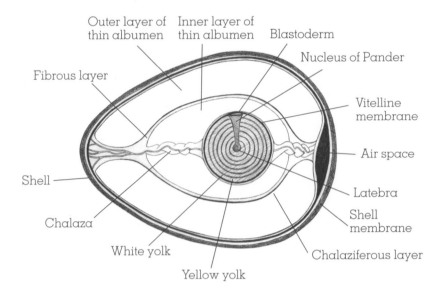

EGG NUTRITION

THE HEALTHY EGG

For a long time it was believed that eating too many eggs could have a detrimental effect on the body's cholesterol level in the blood. However, recent studies have found that this is not the case and that the high nutritional value of eggs outweighs the possible impact on the heart. The studies concluded that eggs are a nutrient-dense food that can significantly contribute to diet quality and that for the majority of people, eating eggs will have little or no influence on cholesterol levels or the risk of coronary heart disease.

Of course, as is the case with any food, no matter how healthy it may be in its natural state, if you cook it in the wrong way you can render it unhealthy – so poach or boil your eggs rather than frying them and thus adding to the amount of fat that you are consuming in your diet.

Eggs are high in protein, low in fat and contain important vitamins for our overall well-being; they are good sources of folic acid, B vitamins, choline, iron, calcium and vitamins A and D, which are found specifically in the yolk. One medium-sized egg can provide a person with 20 per cent of recommended daily allowance of vitamin D and eggs are one of only a few foods to contain it. Low vitamin D levels can cause a whole host of health problems from immune disorders to dementia, poor bone health, arthritis and, researchers now believe, some genetic disorders.

Here is a table of the nutritional values of a medium-sized (approximately 58 g) raw egg. All composition figures relate to the contents excluding the shell.

Constituent of Egg	Amount per egg
Energy	324/78 (kjoules/kcalories)
Protein	6.5 g
Carbohydrate	trace
Fat	5.8 g
Saturated	1.7 g
Monounsaturated	2.3 g
Polyunsaturated	0.9 g
Cholesterol	202 mg
Dietary fibre	0

MINERALS AND TRACE ELEMENTS

Sodium	72 mg
Potassium	67 mg
Calcium	29 mg
Phosphorus	103 mg
Magnesium	6.2 mg
Iron	1.0 mg
Zinc	0.7 mg
Copper	0.04 mg
Iodine	27 µg
Selenium	6 µg
Chlorine	83 mg
Sulphur	83 mg

VITAMINS

Vitamin A	98 µg
Vitamin D	0.9 µg
Vitamin E	0.57 mg
Vitamin C	0
Thamin (Vitamin B_1)	0.05 mg
Riboflavin (Vitamin B_2)	0.24 mg
Niacin	0.05 mg
Vitamin B_6)	0.06 mg
Folate	26 µg
Vitamin B_{12}	1.3 µg
Biotin	10 µg
Pantothenic acid	0.91 mg
Choline[3]	145 mg

PART 9

RECIPES USING EGGS

THE PERFECT BOILED EGG

The perfect boiled egg should have a soft, runny yolk and firm, set white, but this is not always easy to get right. Boiled eggs make a nutritious yet simple breakfast or afternoon tea and children love dipping their 'soldiers' into the middle. Here is one method to get the perfect boiled egg:

1. Use a small saucepan and fill with water to about 5 cm (2 in) in depth. Bring to a rolling boil.

2. Set a timer for 5 minutes. Using a slotted spoon with a long handle, carefully place the eggs in the water. Wait for the water to boil again and then start the timer.

3. While the eggs are cooking, make some toasted and buttered 'soldiers' before the timer goes off.

4. When the time is up, carefully remove the eggs from the saucepan with the slotted spoon and serve straight away in egg cups.

This timing is for a medium egg, so adjust the time to 6 minutes for extra-large eggs or 4 minutes for small ones. Always use a timer – it is no good trying to guess the time, because those extra few seconds can make all the difference.

OMELETTES

An omelette makes a great meal and you can vary it by choosing to cook it as fluffy, non-fluffy or soufflé. It is fun to experiment with the amount of beating because, as you would expect, the more beating you give your mixture the lighter and fluffier your final omelette will become. A soufflé-type omelette is made by beating the egg whites separately and then folding in the yolk, to which a teaspoon of water has been added. Quick and easy to cook, an omelette can be made as versatile as you like by adding extras such as ham, smoked sausage, cheese, mushrooms or mixed vegetables.

1. First, break the eggs into a large bowl (allow 2 medium eggs per person plus 1 for the pan). Now whisk the eggs either with a hand whisk or an electric whisk, making sure you get plenty of air into the mixture so that it becomes fluffy.

2. Once fluffy, add a little water, salt and pepper to taste. You might also like to add some herbs to give it that extra flavour.

3. Add a small amount of olive oil to a frying pan and heat to medium. Gently pour in the mixture and sprinkle your chosen filling over the top.

4. Do not touch at this stage, just allow the bottom layer to cook and solidify. Once it starts to set, pull it back slightly towards the centre of the pan and allow more of the liquid to run to the edge. Keep doing this until all the egg is solid. Finish it off under a hot grill for a few minutes and *voilà* – the perfect omelette.

BREAKFAST MERINGUES

This is a lovely dish to serve for breakfast. It can be accompanied by some ham or smoked salmon for a special occasion.

INGREDIENTS (Serves 6)
6 slices granary bread
6 eggs, separated and at
    room temperature
Hollandaise sauce (see
    page 109)
dash of paprika
chopped parsley
salt and freshly ground
    black pepper

METHOD
1. Preheat the oven to 200°C (400°F/gas mark 6).
2. Cut 6 circles about 10 cm (4 in) in diameter from the slices of granary bread. Place these on a lightly greased baking sheet.

3. In a bowl, beat the egg whites for about 2–3 minutes or until they form stiff peaks. Divide the egg whites over each of the bread circles, using the back of a spoon to form a hollow in the middle of each one. Place an egg yolk in each of the indentations.
4. Bake for about 10–15 minutes or until the egg yolk is set and the white is lightly browned.
5. Remove from the oven and place on individual serving dishes. Drizzle the Hollandaise sauce over the top, then sprinkle with some paprika and chopped parsley. Leave your guests to season with salt and pepper to their own taste.

HOLLANDAISE SAUCE

The secret to a successful Hollandaise sauce is to make sure that it does not get too hot, as overheating will cause the sauce to curdle. A tip to keeping it warm until you are ready to serve it is to rinse a Thermos flask with boiling water and then pour the sauce into the flask. This works well as it keeps it at a nice temperature without causing it to overheat.

INGREDIENTS (Serves 6)

3 egg yolks, at room temperature
1 tbsp freshly squeezed lemon juice
115 g (4 oz) butter
120 ml (4 fl oz) white wine
1 bay leaf
4 peppercorns
1 tbsp white vinegar
salt and freshly ground black pepper

METHOD

1. Stir the egg yolks and lemon juice vigorously in a medium saucepan over a very low heat.

2. Add the butter and white wine and stir continuously with a whisk until the butter has melted.

3. Add the bay leaf, peppercorns, vinegar, salt and pepper. Continue stirring vigorously making sure all the butter has melted and the sauce has thickened. You need to make sure that the butter melts slowly so that the eggs have time to cook and thicken the sauce without the mixture curdling.

4. Keep the sauce warm in a double boiler set over warm (not hot) water until you are ready to serve.

EGGSTRA-SPECIAL SANDWICH

This is a yummy version of a toasted sandwich.

INGREDIENTS (Serves 4)
8 slices sourdough or white
    bread
butter
4 thin slices good-quality ham
4 slices Dutch Edam cheese
4 eggs
finely chopped parsley,
    to garnish

METHOD
1. Spread the butter on one side of each slice of bread. Make 4 sandwiches in the normal way, putting a slice of ham and a slice of cheese in each, then butter the outside of the bread on each side of the sandwich.
2. Heat a large nonstick frying pan on medium heat. Fry each sandwich until the cheese has melted and the

outside is a wonderful golden brown. Remove from the heat and, using a fluted cutter, cut each sandwich into a circle.
3. While the sandwiches are frying, poach the eggs in a saucepan containing at least 7.5 cm (3 in) water to cover the eggs. To prevent them from sticking, grease the bottom of the pan with a little oil first. When the white is cooked but the yolk is still runny, lift out the eggs with a slotted spoon. Make sure all the water has drained from the egg before placing it on top of the sandwich.
4. In a small saucepan, melt a little more butter and mix in the chopped parsley. Drizzle over the top of the eggs and serve immediately on individual plates.

EGGS BAKED IN TOMATO SAUCE

Serving eggs with a tomato sauce makes a wonderful light lunch or supper dish.

INGREDIENTS (Serves 4)
1 tbsp extra virgin olive oil
1 onion, diced
2–3 garlic cloves, minced
400 g (14 oz) can chopped
   tomatoes
2 tsp crushed red pepper
   flakes
2 tsp Italian seasoning
salt and freshly ground
   black pepper
4 eggs
freshly grated Parmesan
   cheese

METHOD
1. Heat the oil in a large frying pan over medium heat. Add the onion and sauté until translucent. Add the garlic and cook for a further 2–3 minutes. Stir in the tomatoes, pepper flakes and Italian seasoning. Season to taste with salt and pepper and cook for a further 2–3 minutes. If you prefer a smooth sauce, whizz the mixture in a blender.
2. Pour your tomato sauce into a frying pan large enough to hold all the eggs. Bring to a simmer and then, one at a time, break each egg into a small cup and slip it carefully into the sauce by lowering the edge of the cup just below the surface.
3. Sprinkle with some Parmesan cheese and cover the pan with a lid. Turn the heat to low and set a timer for exactly 3 minutes.
4. Lift out the eggs carefully and serve over thickly cut crusty bread, pasta, polenta or even mashed potatoes, covered with tomato sauce.

ASPARAGUS AND EGGS

This makes a great lunch or a starter for an evening meal and is very easy to make.

INGREDIENTS (Serves 4)

900 g (2 lb) asparagus spears, cut into 12–15 cm (5–6 in) lengths

freshly grated Parmesan cheese

60 g (2 oz) butter

4 eggs

salt and freshly ground black pepper

METHOD

1. Snap off the tough ends of the asparagus and then cook in boiling, salted water for approximately 4–5 minutes until they are tender but still crisp.

2. Drain the asparagus and lay on several thicknesses of paper towel to remove excessive moisture.

3. Divide the asparagus among 4 individual serving plates and sprinkle generously with Parmesan.

4. In a medium-sized frying pan, heat the butter until it sizzles when a drip of water is dropped into it. Break the shells and carefully slip the eggs into the pan. Reduce the heat to low and cook for 2–3 minutes or until the whites are set and the yolks are still runny.

5. Remove the eggs with a spatula, being careful not to break the yolk. Place the eggs on top of the asparagus.

6. Increase the heat under the frying pan and cook until the butter is slightly browned. Pour this over the top of the eggs and then season with salt and freshly ground black pepper. Serve immediately.

SPANISH EGGS WITH CHORIZO

This is a typical recipe from Extremadura in western Spain.

INGREDIENTS (Serves 4)
5 tbsp olive oil
2 onions, finely chopped
salt and freshly ground
   black pepper
400 g (14 oz) can chopped
   tomatoes
1 tsp oregano
1 tsp sugar
4 medium-sized baking
   potatoes, cut into wedges
300 g (10 oz) chorizo, thinly
   sliced
100 g (3½ oz) peas
4 eggs
handful of fresh parsley

METHOD
1. In a heavy-based frying pan, heat up 1 tbsp olive oil and gently fry the onion until soft.
2. Add the salt and pepper and fry until the onion is crisp and golden brown.
3. Once the onion is cooked add the tomatoes, oregano and sugar and cook on a gentle heat, stirring regularly, for 5 minutes.
4. In a shallow frying pan, heat the rest of the olive oil and fry the potatoes gently for 10 minutes, turning regularly.
5. While the potatoes are frying add the chorizo and peas to the tomatoes and onion and cook for 5–10 minutes.
6. Once the potatoes are ready add them to the pan and mix well.
7. Crack the eggs on top of the mixture and leave to gently cook until the egg white has solidified, but the yolk is still runny.
8. Season again with salt and pepper, garnish with parsley and serve with crusty bread.

RASPBERRY CRÈME BRÛLÉE

This is a raspberry version of this traditional egg dessert.

INGREDIENTS (Serves 6)
500 ml (16 fl oz) double cream
1 vanilla pod
3 egg yolks
2 whole eggs
100 g (3½ oz) caster sugar
150 g (5½ oz) raspberries

METHOD

1. Pre-heat the oven to 180°C (350°F/gas mark 4).

2. Split the vanilla pod and scrape out the seeds. Add these and the pod to a pan containing the cream and bring to the boil.

3. As soon as it reaches boiling point, turn off the heat and leave to infuse for 5 minutes.

4. In a mixing bowl, cream the eggs and sugar together until light and fluffy.

5. Turn the heat on again and bring the cream back to the boil. Pour it on to the egg and sugar mixture and whisk until it starts to thicken slightly.

6. Sieve the mixture into a jug and pour into 6 ramekins.

7. Drop about 8 raspberries on top of each ramekin and then place them in a roasting tray filled with cool water so that it reaches halfway up the ramekin.

8. Place the tray on the middle shelf of the oven and bake for approximately 30 minutes, until set.

9. Once set, remove from the oven and leave to cool for 1 hour before placing in the fridge until required.

10. Just before serving, sprinkle each brûlée with caster sugar and place under a hot grill for a couple of minutes until the sugar caramelizes.

PART 10

BREEDING

INTRODUCING A COCKEREL TO YOUR FLOCK

The natural progression for many people who keep chickens for eggs and/or meat is to start breeding their own chicks by introducing a cockerel into the flock of females. This has to be done with care, as choosing the wrong cockerel could mean disaster. Also, if you are keeping your hens in an urban environment you should think very carefully before buying a cockerel as he may well be considered a noise nuisance by your neighbours.

A heavy-breed cockerel should be at least 10 months old before he is given the task of breeding with your hens and he should also have no more than eight hens to contend with. The lighter breeds can cope with up to 10 hens. Ideally, you should try to obtain a cockerel that is the same breed as the hens you intend him to mate with. However, you should check that he is not actually related to any of your hens as inbreeding can cause genetic problems and deformities for future offspring.

GOOD BREEDING STOCK

When choosing your cockerel, look for certain markers in his appearance that will help you to know if he is fit and healthy:

- His wattles and comb should be bright red in colour.

- His coat should be shiny and glossy and his feet smooth and straight (see panel opposite).

- He should have a confident gait, walking with a strut.

HEN HINT

A very useful marker for knowing if your cockerel is going to be a good performer is the appearance of his feet. The skin on them should be smooth and the toes straight. Although this does not have a direct bearing on the cockerel's fertility, it does affect his health and the way in which he mates with the hen. Smooth skin will not be as prone to infection and straight toes will help to keep him balanced when they touch vent to vent. If the cockerel and hen are unbalanced and do not connect properly, fertilization may not take place.

Temperament is a very important consideration when choosing a cockerel, especially if there will be young children around. Not only do cockerels have an unpleasant peck, they are also able to jump more than 1 m (3¼ ft) from the ground, kicking with their feet and spurs when threatened. If you buy a young male you need to keep a watching eye on his temperament as even though he may seem placid at purchase, matters may change during the breeding season. Choosing your male from a non-aggressive breed means that he should be genetically calm, but there will always be exceptions to the rule as all birds are individuals.

Once you have chosen a suitable cockerel for the job you will probably keep him for 4–5 years as he will be in his prime for this amount of time. A particularly strong cockerel may even continue to mate for up to six years, so be prepared for him to be a member of your extended family for some time.

It is best to purchase a cockerel from a reputable breeder as they should have records of the bird's parentage and it will help you to judge if he comes from a good strain, is resistant to disease and is relatively non-aggressive. Take time to research the different breeds (see pages 10–16) before going ahead with a breeding programme, ensuring that the breed of your choice is known for its placid disposition.

INTRODUCING YOUR NEW COCKEREL TO HIS HAREM

A cockerel will live comfortably with a group of hens but he should still be introduced to the flock gradually, as should any new addition, male or female. You need to accustom him to his new surroundings just as much as you need to habituate your flock to having a male around.

More often than not the male will go to the top of the pecking order and take charge over his females, but this is not always the case as an older female with this status may not simply hand it over to a teenage cockerel. However, in time, natural selection will more than likely determine the cockerel to be top bird.

BREEDING STOCK

Over the time you have kept your hens and got to know them individually you will have become aware of which ones are the best layers – that is to say, those which lay most frequently and produce the highest-quality eggs. Once you have chosen your breeding stock these birds should ideally be fed a breeder diet that will include the right levels of protein, vitamins and minerals to ensure the healthiest chicks possible. It is also important that the hens chosen for breeding are not lacking vitamin E, as this can lead to chicks having what is commonly known as 'crazy chick' disease. A chick suffering from this disorder will not be able to coordinate its movements, will suffer from tremors and will only be able to look upwards.

Once your hens have been chosen you may want to segregate your breeders and cockerel from the rest of your laying flock so each does its job correctly. This way your hens will be eating the correct type of feed required for laying or breeding and your cockerel will not be wasting time trying to mate with birds of a lesser standard. Nevertheless, do keep them within viewing distance of each other and allow them to mingle every day so that they know they are still part of the same flock.

Once your hens have mated with the cockerel a few times the eggs they start to produce will be fertilized. For the egg to stand a chance of developing further the hen needs to sustain a constant body temperature of around 39.8°C (103.5°F) and also needs to be feeling broody – though once you have some fertilized eggs you can always rear them in an artificial incubator (see pages 22–29) instead if the hen does not do the job.

BREEDING WITH A BROODY HEN

Just because a hen has been mated by a cockerel and lays an egg that is fertilized, it does not mean that she is necessarily in the right frame of mind for sitting on her eggs and rearing them from egg to chick and to pullet. The tell-tale signs of a broody hen are discussed on pages 71–72, but whereas those pages looked at ways of preventing broodiness, when you wish to breed from a hen it is something that needs to be encouraged.

Waiting for one of your flock to go broody is probably your best bet. She will lay eggs on a daily basis and then stop when she is ready to start the incubation process. You can then either let her sit solely on her own eggs or choose the best eggs from the whole of the breeding stock – she will not be fussy.

> ## HEN HINT
>
> Silkie crossbreeds – such as the Silkie Sussex and the Silkie Wyandotte – make the best brooders. If you want to start breeding regularly you could always keep a few of these chickens in a pen alongside your chosen layer or dual-purpose breed and use them solely for the purpose of hatching the other birds' eggs.

It is a good idea to move your broody hen away from the rest of the flock before she actually starts sitting. There are a couple of reasons for this: first, the other hens may start laying their own eggs in the nest and you will have to constantly remove them as they will all be at different stages, and secondly, it will help you judge just how insistent she is on completing the task in hand; you want to be sure that your broody hen is not going to give up halfway through. Once you have ascertained that she definitely is broody, the process can begin. She will need a broody coop, but almost anything can be used for this – a cardboard box in a shed or garage will do, as long as the hen and her potential hatch are safe from predators such as foxes and rats.

Once eggs are in place and your hen is sitting comfortably, you can just let nature take its course. Do ensure though that she leaves her nest once a day to be fed and watered, and to defecate. Try to arrange this at the same time each day so that she accepts it as routine and does not become anxious every day about having to leave her nest. You can also use this period to clean out any droppings from the brooding box and check that the eggs she is sitting on are still in good condition.

HATCHING AND REARING

Chicken eggs take 21 days to hatch and, unlike artificial incubating in which you need to turn the eggs at least five times a day for the first 18 days, a broody hen will instinctively do this herself. It not only ensures that the embryos develop properly but also helps to keep an even distribution of warmth and gives the egg access to the right amount of oxygen. On days 19–21 you can intervene by sprinkling the eggs (without touching them) sparingly with warm water as this helps to keep the membranes that surround the embryo moist.

MOTHER HEN

Once the eggs have hatched the broody hen will naturally

take on the role of mother, whether the chicks are her own or not. Newborn chicks must be left in the broody coop until they are at least one week old. The mother hen will soon teach her young how to feed and drink, but keep an eye on their progress and make sure that they are kept away from draughts.

For the first few weeks the chicks will have to be shut in at night and kept separate from the rest of the flock. By week three, the chicks will be old enough to spend their days in an outside run with their mother but will need to be vaccinated before being introduced to the rest of the flock. See pages 34–39 for more information on new-born chicks.

PART 11

CULLING AND PREPARING

KILLING CHICKENS FOR CONSUMPTION

If you are keeping broilers or dual-purpose breeds there will come a time when you need to dispatch a hen in order to get your meat. Broilers are bred to grow at a faster rate than layers or dual-purpose strains, and will be ready for culling at 6–8 weeks of age. However, the best thing to use as a gauge is the bird's weight – 2 kg (4.5 lb) is ideal.

Dual-purpose breeds take a few weeks longer to get up to a decent table weight, but if you are keeping them for eggs as well you may only want to use them for meat after they have had their first egg-laying cycle. Chickens such as these are sometimes referred to as 'spent layers' and in commercial chicken farming would be used for soups, stocks and pies. However, they are fine for the table if you are just raising a few in your backyard.

For many people who keep chickens at home, however much they like the idea of being self-sufficient in the egg and meat department, the idea of killing a bird can be very intimidating and unpleasant. If it is an act that you really cannot bring yourself to carry out, take your bird to your nearest poultry expert, who will know exactly how to do it with the best interests of the chicken being paramount.

HUMANE CULLING

Chickens bred for meat should be taken off their feed approximately 12 hours before they are slaughtered. This allows the crop and intestinal tract time to empty, as a full digestive system increases the chances of contamination during the removal of the viscera from the carcass. They should, however, be given fresh water right up to the last moment.

Birds should be collected from their coop after dark using a warm red light. This will help keep the hen calm and will help avoid frightening the other birds.

The main thing when culling a bird from your flock is to make sure that you are mentally prepared for the task in hand and that you undertake the task in an appropriate and swift way. Hesitation and uncertainty about the procedure will lead to unnecessary pain and anxiety for your bird. The following steps will help to make culling as painless and humane as possible:

- Remain calm – if the bird senses you are nervous it too will become distressed. Gently pick up the bird from its box and talk to it quietly the whole time. Ensure that the bird is held securely. (Through the act of keeping chickens you should have already made your birds comfortable with being handled, so this part of the procedure should not give them a nasty surprise).

- Cup the top of the chicken's head in the palm of your hand, ensuring that your middle fingers are pointing away from the beak.

- Forcefully pull downwards on the head and twist in one clean movement. This breaks the chicken's neck and you will feel the head part from the body.

- Release the pressure. The bird will start to flap its wings vigorously, but do not worry – it cannot feel anything, as the nervous system between the brain

and the body has been
interrupted. You can be
assured that the bird will be
dead within 15 seconds.

• Finally, hang your bird over
a bucket from its feet so that
its head is pointing towards
the floor – this means that the
blood will pool in the neck.
Make an incision in the bird's
jugular and allow the blood
to drain into the bucket.

PLUCKING AND PREPARING

Once the bird has been hung
and the blood drained you
can pluck the feathers by
filling a clean, disinfected
bucket with boiling water
and placing the bird in it for
about 60 seconds. Remove
the bird from the water and
begin plucking, using your
fingers. The feathers should
come out of the skin easily
as the hot water melts the fat
around their roots, making
them almost fall out. If there
are any parts that prove
difficult to pluck, dunk the bird
in the hot water again. The
next step is evisceration. This
is the removal of the chicken's
internal organs, especially
those in the abdominal
cavity such as the intestines.
This is something that gets
easier with practice. Here are
the basic steps to follow to
prepare your bird:

• If you are going to be
preparing your chicken

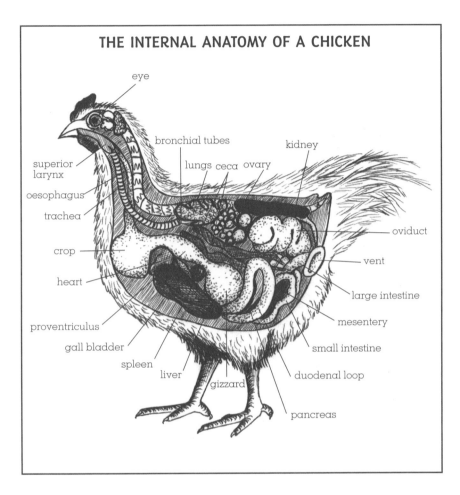

THE INTERNAL ANATOMY OF A CHICKEN

eye

bronchial tubes

kidney

superior larynx

lungs ceca ovary

oesophagus

trachea

oviduct

crop

vent

heart

large intestine

proventriculus

mesentery

gall bladder

small intestine

spleen

liver

duodenal loop

gizzard

pancreas

directly after plucking you may wish to dunk it in a bucket of cold water to bring the temperature down first.

• Remove the chicken's feet, using a sharp knife. If you

wish to use as much of your bird as possible, the feet can be skinned and used in a broth or stock.

• Cut a slit up the back of the neck to the head so

CHICKEN CHAT

The world record for plucking a chicken completely is 4.4 seconds. Obviously it will take a beginner longer – you can anticipate taking 20 minutes or so to carry out this task properly.

that you can peel the neck skin off. Then cut below the crop (the pouch in a bird's gullet where food is stored and prepared for digestion) and remove both the crop and the windpipe from the carcass.

- Cut off the neck at the base and save it for making soup or stock.

- Make an incision between the bird's vent and tail, making sure that you do not sever the rectum. Cut right round the rectum, ensuring that it is removed without being sliced into, otherwise the meat will taste bitter.

- Carefully pull the vent, and the attached guts, out of the tail end. The gizzard, lungs and heart will follow. These can all be used in the kitchen, but if you do wish to use the liver ensure that you locate and remove the gall bladder (a small greenish organ) first.

- Lastly, rinse the chicken in cold water and put in the refrigerator for a few hours prior to cooking.

When you have done all the hard work, you can enjoy eating your own chicken using one of the recipes in the next section.

PART 12
CHICKEN RECIPES

CHILLI CHICKEN

This is a wonderful variation on the traditional chilli con carne and is very quick to make. It can be served with nachos that have been topped with melted cheese.

INGREDIENTS (Serves 4)

500–600 g (1 lb 2 oz–1 lb 5 oz) boneless chicken, cut into 2.5 cm (1 in) cubes
2 tbsp soy sauce
2 tbsp cornflour
salt to taste
1 egg
oil for deep-frying
2 garlic cloves, minced
5–6 green chillies
500 ml (16 fl oz) chicken stock
1 tsp sugar
½ tsp white pepper
2 spring onions, finely chopped

METHOD

1. Marinate the chicken pieces in a mixture of 1 tbsp soy sauce, 1 tbsp cornflour, salt and the egg for around 30 minutes.

2. Pour enough oil into a deep pan to cover the chicken pieces and fry until they are golden brown.

3. In a wok or large frying pan, heat 1 tbsp oil and add the garlic and green chillies. Sauté for a few seconds.

4. Add the chicken stock, bring to the boil and add the sugar, white pepper, salt and remaining soy sauce. Add the fried chicken and cook for a few minutes.

5. Dissolve the remaining cornflour in a little cold water and add to the chilli, stirring to avoid any lumps. Cook for a further 5 minutes.

6. Serve the chilli garnished with chopped spring onions and accompanied by a bowl of steamed or boiled rice.

CHICKEN MYERS

Do not be deterred by the melange of ingredients in this recipe – the end result is a taste sensation.

INGREDIENTS (Serves 5–6)

4 large chicken breasts, cut into thirds
2 broccoli heads
2 × 400 g (14 oz) cans of condensed chicken soup
400 g (14 oz) can of condensed mushroom soup
6 tbsp mayonnaise
3 tbsp double cream
2 tsp garam masala
2 tsp mild chilli powder
Freshly ground black pepper
150 g (5½ oz) Cheddar cheese, grated

METHOD

1. Preheat the oven to 200°C (400°F/gas mark 6).
2. Place the chicken pieces into a large oven-proof dish.
3. Cut the broccoli, including the stalks, into smaller pieces and stir it into the chicken.
4. In a separate bowl, mix together the soup, mayonnaise, cream and spices and then spoon evenly over the chicken and broccoli.
5. Season with black pepper (there should be enough salt in the soup) and then place in the oven and cook for approximately 30 minutes, or until the chicken is cooked.
6. Remove from the oven and sprinkle with the grated cheese. Return to the oven and cook until the cheese becomes crisp and golden and starts to bubble.
7. Serve immediately with jacket potatoes or rice and a side salad.

QUICK CHICKEN CURRY

Curries are such easy things to make as everything is cooked in one pot. They can also be one of the most healthy ways to eat if you avoid too much clarified butter and cream. Chicken lends itself well to curry as it is not a strong-tasting meat so will pick up the flavours of the herbs and spices. This recipe is quick and healthy, and so flavoursome that you may want to throw the take-away menu in the bin!

INGREDIENTS (Serves 4)

2 tbsp corn oil or olive oil
1 large onion, finely chopped
4 garlic cloves, chopped
2 fresh red chillies, deseeded and finely chopped
2 tsp garam masala
2 tsp ground cumin
2 tsp ground coriander
1 tsp ground turmeric

2 tsp hot chilli powder
2 × 400 g (14 oz) cans chopped tomatoes
3 large skinless chicken breasts cut into 2.5 cm (1 in) cubes
2 red peppers, chopped
4 fresh tomatoes, cut into wedges (the skins can be removed if you prefer)
10 curry leaves
8 cardamon pods
1 cinnamon stick (6 cm/2½ in long)
100 ml (3½ fl oz) natural yoghurt

METHOD

1. Heat 1 tbsp oil in a wok or heavy-based frying pan and add the onion, garlic and fresh chilli. Fry gently until soft and translucent, taking care that they do not burn.

2. Add the garam masala, cumin, coriander, turmeric

and chilli powder and fry for a further 2 minutes until they are aromatic. The spices will cover the onion, garlic and chilli and form a kind of dry paste.

3. Add the tomatoes and fry for about 2 minutes so that everything is thoroughly mixed, making a sauce. Remove from the heat.

4. Transfer the sauce to a blender, whizz until smooth and place to one side.

5. In the same wok or frying pan heat up the remaining oil and add the chicken. Fry the chicken for 5 minutes before adding the chopped peppers

and fresh tomatoes. Fry for a further 2 minutes.

6. Transfer the blended sauce back to the pan and add the curry leaves, cardamon pods and cinnamon stick. Bring to the boil and then turn the heat down to medium, cover and simmer for 20 minutes, allowing all the flavours to infuse.

7. Uncover and stir in the natural yoghurt (this can be to taste depending on how mild you want it to be). Add the coriander.

8. Serve with boiled rice and naan bread.

TASTY ROAST CHICKEN

There are many different ways to roast a chicken – but this simple recipe using lemon and fresh herbs is very refreshing on the palate.

INGREDIENTS (Serves 4–6)
1 chicken (approximately 1.5 kg/3 lb 3 oz)
3 tbsp olive oil
2 handfuls of fresh basil, torn
a small bunch of rosemary
6 bay leaves
6 garlic cloves
sea salt and freshly ground black pepper
1 lemon

METHOD
1. If your chicken has been refrigerated, take it out 30 minutes prior to preparing.
2. Preheat the oven to 190°C (375°F/gas mark 5) and put 2 tablespoons of oil in a roasting tin and place in the oven.

3. With the cavity of the chicken facing you, carefully place your fingers under the skin, being careful not to pierce it. Once the skin is lifted slightly away from the meat, place a handful of your fresh herbs either side of the spine and flatten the skin back down.
4. Using a sharp knife, make a few incisions in each of the legs and stuff with some more of the herbs.
5. Take two of your garlic cloves, peel them and rub all over the chicken skin, discarding them when finished. Follow by brushing the remainder of the oil over the skin and season well with sea salt and black pepper.
6. Cut your lemon in half and squeeze the juice from one half over the chicken.
7. Place the rest of the herbs, together with the other half of

the lemon and the remaining garlic cloves (with the peel still on), inside the cavity of the bird.

8. Remove the roasting tin from the oven, ensure that the oil is evenly dispersed and place the bird inside, breast side down. Return to the oven and cook for a couple of minutes before turning the chicken on to its other breast. Cook for a further 2 minutes and then turn the bird over and cook for 20 minutes per 450 g (1 lb), plus an extra 10 to 20 minutes.

9. If you wish to roast any vegetables or potatoes together with the chicken, these should be added to the tray for the last 45 minutes of cooking. Baste the bird at this time and also halfway through cooking the vegetables. If the vegetables are drying out, add a couple of tablespoons of water to the roasting tray.

10. When it is time to remove the chicken from the oven, check that the juices run clear by inserting a skewer into one of the legs.

11. Remove the bird and turn the heat down to 150°C (300°F/ gas mark 2) so the vegetables continue to cook slowly.

12. Place the chicken on a board and cover with kitchen foil. Leave to rest for approximately 15 minutes. Meanwhile, make your gravy, using the juices in the roasting tin.

TOM YUM CHICKEN NOODLE SOUP

This spicy soup is perfect for using up your leftover roast chicken (see previous page).

INGREDIENTS (Serves 4)
Leftover roast chicken
1 litre (1¾ pints) vegetable
   stock or chicken stock
2 kaffir lime leaves
1 stalk lemongrass, bruised
2 tsp fresh root ginger, grated
4 red chillies, sliced
150 g (5½ oz) button
   mushrooms, halved
150 g (5½ oz) shiitake
   mushrooms
300 g (10½ oz) baby sweetcorn,
   cut into thirds
200 g (7 oz) medium egg
   noodles, broken into
   small pieces
1 tbsp fish sauce
1 tbsp chilli sauce
50 g (1¾ oz) beansprouts
handful of fresh coriander,
   chopped

METHOD
1. Remove as much meat as possible from the chicken carcass.
2. Put the chicken or vegetable stock in a saucepan and add the lime leaves, lemongrass and ginger. Bring to the boil.
3. Add the chillies, mushrooms and baby sweetcorn and simmer gently for about 3 minutes.
4. Add the chicken and simmer for another 6 minutes.
5. While the soup is simmering, bring another saucepan of water to the boil and cook your noodles according to the instructions on the packet.
6. Stir in the fish and chilli sauce to the soup and remove from the heat. Drain your noodles and add to them to the soup.
7. Serve in bowls, garnished with beansprouts and a sprinkling of coriander.

CHICKEN GOUJONS

Here is a recipe for the kids that will be far tastier than anything you can buy at the supermarket.

INGREDIENTS (Serves 4–6)
1 garlic clove, minced
100 g (3½ oz) butter, melted
60 g (2 oz) fresh breadcrumbs, dried
50 g (1¾ oz) Parmesan cheese, grated
2 tbsp fresh parsley, chopped
grated zest of 1 lemon
salt and freshly ground black pepper
900 g (2 lb) skinless, boneless chicken breast, cut into strips

METHOD
1. Preheat the oven to 230°C (450°F/gas mark 8).
2. In a large bowl, combine the minced garlic with the melted butter.

3. In another bowl, combine the breadcrumbs, Parmesan, parsley, lemon zest, salt and pepper.
4. Dip each chicken piece into the garlic butter and then into the crumb mixture until they are thoroughly coated.
5. Place the coated chicken pieces on a baking tray, leaving a little space between each piece. Drizzle with the remaining garlic butter and cook, uncovered, for 15 minutes or until the chicken is cooked through. Turn halfway through cooking to make sure the pieces brown evenly.

MOROCCAN CHICKEN TAGINE

Here is an exotic taste of Morocco. The recipe uses a spice blend called 'ras el hanout' which literally means 'king of the spices'. In Morocco, this blend varies but the main flavours stay constant and typical of the country. Below is a refined yet traditional mix that works perfectly with the chicken tagine recipe.

FOR THE RAS EL HANOUT INGREDIENTS

2 tsp ground cumin

2 tsp ground ginger

2 tsp ground turmeric

1 tsp ground cinnamon

1 tsp ground coriander seeds

1 tsp ground allspice

1 tsp nutmeg

1 tsp freshly ground black pepper

½ tsp ground sea salt

½ tsp ground star anise

½ tsp ground cloves

METHOD

Mix all the spices together in a small bowl. Transfer to an airtight container and use as required. By keeping your spice blend in an airtight container or jar and storing at room temperature it should last approximately 3 months.

FOR THE TAGINE
INGREDIENTS (Serves 4)

2 tbsp olive oil

1 large onion, thinly sliced

2 garlic cloves, mashed

1 red chilli, finely chopped and deseeded

1 red pepper, cut into 4 cm (1½ in) strips

1 orange pepper, cut into 4 cm (1½ in) strips

2 courgettes, cut into 2 cm (¾ in) slices

8 chicken thighs, skinned

2 large flavoursome tomatoes, skinned and roughly chopped

4 tsp ras el hanout (see
opposite page)
400 g (14 oz) can of chickpeas,
drained
100 g (3½ oz) sultanas
600 ml (1 pint) chicken stock
400 g (14 oz) couscous

METHOD

1. Preheat the oven to 200°C
(400°F/gas mark 6).
2. Heat the oil in a large wok
or saucepan and lightly
fry the onion, garlic, chilli,
peppers and courgettes until
they just start to soften.
3. Add the chicken and lightly
fry for a further 5 minutes
before adding the tomatoes.
4. Fry for a further 2 minutes,
until the tomatoes break up
into a pulp and release
their juices.
5. Stir in the ras el hanout,

chickpeas, sultanas and
chicken stock. Remove from
the hob and transfer to a
traditional tagine or
casserole dish.
6. Place in the oven and
cook for 20 minutes, or until
the meat is cooked through.
Meanwhile, cook the
couscous according to
packet instructions.
7. Serve the tagine with
steamed couscous and a
warm flat bread.

OTHER OPTIONS

Replace the sultanas with
either prunes or apricots.

Serve the tagine with a side
dish of roasted vegetables,
such as sweet peppers,
courgette, aubergine, squash
and onions.

GLOSSARY

Bantam A small type of chicken. Most breeds now have a bantam alternative, about 25 per cent the size of the regular breed.

Bloom The protective coating of an eggshell. It protects the embryo during the incubation process and also while storing as food. Note that it can easily be removed, so keep handling to a minimum and do not wash your eggs until you are about to use them unless they are soiled.

Breeding stock Hens that produce the best quality eggs that you wish your cockerel to mate with.

Broiler A young chicken bred specifically for its meat.

Brooder A heated house used to keep chicks in the first weeks of their lives if no hen is available to raise them.

Broody A hen displaying the instinct to incubate eggs.

Candling The process of checking an egg with a light to see if it is fertilized.

Cannibalism The act of pecking, tearing and consuming of skin, tissues or organs of flock mates, or when a chicken eats its own eggs.

Chick A baby chicken.

Cock A male chicken over 12 months old.

Cockerel An adolescent male.

Comb The red, fleshy crest on the top of a chicken's head (more prominent on males).

Cluck A short, low sound, usually a sign of contentment.

Crop The pouch in a bird's gullet where food is stored and prepared for digestion.

Deep littering The method of layering droppings with wood-shavings and paper shreddings in a coop which is then cleaned out every spring and the litter used for compost.

Dual-purpose Chicken breeds that lay good-quality eggs and can also be used for meat.

Dust bath Rather than bathing in water, chickens take dust baths which help to maintain their feathers in good condition and also keep them cool.

Embryo The unhatched chick.

Flight feathers The under feathers at the front of the wing. They are usually longer and darker in colour than the other feathers.

Flock A group of chickens.

Forced-air Describes an artificial incubator for hatching eggs that uses a fan.

Free-range Chickens kept in a natural environment with freedom of movement.

Grit Solid mineral particles fed to chickens to aid their digestion.

H5N1 Influenza A virus subtype H5N1, also known as 'bird flu'.

Hatchling A newborn chick.

Hen A female chicken.

Husbandry The care, cultivation and breeding of chickens (or other animals and crops).

Hybrid A chicken that is a mix of more than one breed.

Infundibulum A funnel-shaped organ, part of the hen's reproductive system.

Mash A food mix containing the necessary nutrients a chicken needs at a specific point in its life.

Nest box Place where a chicken lays her eggs.

Parasite An animal or vegetable that lives on and obtains nourishment from a host animal or vegetable, usually with detrimental effect.

Perch A support provided so that a chicken can roost above ground.

Point of lay The transition stage between adolescent hen and full-fledged layer.

Pop-hole A small door within the coop that the chickens use for exit and entry.

Pullet An adolescent hen.

Roost The place where chickens settle for the night.

Rooster Another term for a cock – a fully-grown male chicken.

Salmonella A bacteria that can cause food-poisoning.

Scratch When a chicken turns the ground over with its feet in the search for seeds, grit, insects or plants to eat.

Sexing Defining where your chicks are male or female.

Sex-linked Hybrid chicken breeds with specially bred feathers that differ between the male and the female.

Shaft The hollow quill of a feather that runs down the centre.

Spent layer A hen that has produced eggs for one complete cycle and is now to be used for meat.

Spur A hard spike on the back of the cock's leg, used for fighting.

Still-air incubator An artificial incubator for hatching eggs that does not use a fan.

Toxoplasmosis A disease caused by a parasitic spore transmitted through undercooked meat, soil and animal faeces.

Turning The process of gently rotating eggs that are being artificially incubated. This needs to be done about five times a day until day 18.

Vent The anus of the chicken that serves for both excretion and reproduction.

Vent sexing Distinguishing whether a chick is male or female by checking for a lump on its vent.

Wing clipping Cutting the flight feathers on one of the chicken's wings in order to limit its flight capacity.

Worming Treating your flock with a powder or medicine as prevention against, or cure for, worms.

Yolk The yellow internal part of an egg which nourishes the developing embryo. When the chick hatches there is still enough 'yolk', now within its body, to sustain it for up to 48 hours.

INDEX